D0983936

HIGH PERFORMANCE LOUDSPEAKERS

To Marianne

HIGH PERFORMANCE LOUDSPEAKERS

MARTIN COLLOMS, *B.Sc.(Hons.)*

(Second Edition)

PENTECH PRESS
London : Plymouth

First published 1978
by Pentech Press Limited,
Estover Road, Plymouth,
Devon PL6 7PZ

ISBN 0 7273 0803 3 (Cloth)
    0 7273 0804 1 (Paper)

First edition   1978
Second edition 1980
Reprinted   **1981**

British Library Cataloguing in Publication Data
Colloms, Martin
    High performance loudspeakers. — 2nd ed.
    1. High-fidelity sound systems
    2. Loud-speakers
    I. Title
    621.389'33   TK7881.7

    ISBN 0-7273-0803-3
    ISBN 0-7273-0804-1 Pbk

Set by Mid-County Press,
2a Merivale Road, London SW15 2NW
Printed and bound in Great Britain by
Billing & Sons Limited,
Guildford, London and Worcester

Contents

Preface to the Second Edition

For the second edition the original material has been carefully revised and where necessary clarified to cover all the important developments that have occurred since the first edition was begun in 1976 and the references and bibliography correspondingly extended.

New or revised topics include: low cost Fourier analysis systems; sub-woofers; integrated room/speaker design; 24dB/octave acoustic crossover developments; the control of low-frequency distortion and advances in the subjective testing of loudspeakers.

Martin Colloms
July 1979

Preface

A high quality loudspeaker is required to reproduce sound with sufficient fidelity to satisfy a critical audience when fed from an accurate electrical signal. It is immaterial whether the listeners are numbered in thousands or comprise only a few individuals: loudspeaker systems can be designed to cater for both situations without compromising the basic standard of performance.

There are thus numerous applications for high quality loudspeakers. For example, broadcast and recording engineers rely heavily on monitor loudspeakers in order to critically analyse the quality of the programme they are producing. Other applications range in scope from the rock festival to the concert and opera hall, and in size from a theatre auditorium to an ordinary living room. Reinforcement loudspeakers are commonly used for sound amplification in live performances today, and while specialised systems are employed for instruments such as an electric guitar, other wider range sounds such as voice and woodwind require high performance speakers with a capability to allow the reproduced level to match that of the accompanying brass or a modern drum kit. Theatres and opera houses often use quality systems for off-stage sound effects, and many of today's star performers would be unable to reach a large audience without the aid of a microphone and quality amplify-system. Special techniques are however required to attain the acoustic outputs necessary to satisfy a large stadium audience, and high efficiency, stacked, horn loaded, directional arrays are commonly employed for this purpose.

The author's aim is to provide an up-to-date analysis and review of high performance loudspeaker techniques. Although it is not intended to be an exhaustive work, reference has been made in the text to original research material including the most important modern work in the field. Precedence is accorded to the moving coil drive unit, as this is by far the most widely used, although some coverage is also given to other viable if less common devices. In addition to the fundamentals — relevant acoustic theory, transducer design, enclosures, acoustic loading, etc. — space is also accorded to developments in electronic crossover design and active speaker systems, as well as to the latest measurement techniques and such controversial questions as linear phase. By using the references supplied, the book can be used as the basis for further research, and as such, not only high fidelity enthusiasts should find it of interest, but also students studying such subjects as electronics, electroacoustics, broadcasting and recording. Even the design engineer and technical author may find it a useful appraisal of current techniques and a convenient source of subject references.

Symbols

A_g	Magnet gap area
A_m	Magnet area
a	Piston radius
a_g	Magnet gap radius
α	Compliance ratio $(=C_{AS}/C_{AB})$
B, B_g	Magnetic flux density in the coil and air gap
c	Velocity of sound, (345 m/s in air)
C_{AB}	Acoustic compliance of enclosure volume
C_{AS}	Acoustic compliance of suspension
C_{AT}	Total acoustic compliance of driver and enclosure
C_{MEC}	Electrical capacitance equivalent of moving mass $(=M_{AC}S_D^2/B^2l^2)$
C_{MS}	Total suspension compliance of driver
E_g	Generator (amplifier) voltage
F	Force
f	Frequency in Hz
f_B	Helmholtz resonance of vented box
f_c	System resonance, driver in closed box
f_o or f_s	Free air resonance of driver
f_3	−3 dB cutoff frequency
g	Gravitational acceleration
$G(S)$	Response function
H	Coercive force, magnetic flux
h	System tuning ratio $(=f_B/f_s)$
I	Current in coil
K_B, k_H	Magnetic loss factors
k_n	Reference band efficiency factor
k_p	Power constant
l	Length of motor coil wire immersed in magnetic gap field
L_c	Inductance of motor coil
L_{CEB}	Electrical inductance equivalent of box volume compliance
L_{CES}	Electrical inductance equivalent of driver suspension compliance
L_{CET}	Electrical inductance equivalent of system compliance $(=C_{AT}B^2l^2/S_D^2)$
M_c	Mass of motor coil
M_{EC}	Acoustic mass of driver diaphragm assembly including air load
M_D	Total driver moving mass, (excluding air load)
M_{AC}	Acoustic mass of driver and air load fitted in enclosure
M_{AS}	Acoustic mass of driver and air load
n	Number of turns
ω	Angular frequency $= 2\pi f$
P	Sound power
Q	Ratio of reactance to resistance (series circuit) or resistance to reactance (parallel circuit) (or directivity factor)

Q_T	Driver total Q
Q_E	Electrical Q of driver
Q_M	Mechanical Q of driver
Q_{TC}	Working Q of system of driver and enclosure
ρ_0	Density of air (=1.18 kg/m^3)
R	Resistance (electrical)
R_{EC}	$=B^2l^2/(R_{AB} + R_{AS})S_D^2$ electrical equivalent of mechanical losses
R_{AB}	Enclosure loss acoustic resistance
R_C	Resistance of motor coil
R_{MA}	Resistive component of air load radiation impedance
R_{MS}	Suspension mechanical resistance
r	Distance from source
S_D	Effective projected diaphragm area
s.p.l.	Sound pressure level
θ	Angle from source axis
U_C	Diaphragm or coil axial velocity
V_{AS}	Equivalent closed air volume of driver compliance, C_{MS}
V_B	Box or enclosure volume
X_{MA}	Reactive mass component of air load radiation impedance
Z_{MA}	Air load radiation impedance; $R_{MA} + jX_{MA}$
η_0	System reference efficiency (Power in/power out into 2π field) in level range.

1

General review

This chapter is not intended to provide a complete history of the loudspeaker, as apart from taking up too much space, this subject is adequately covered elsewhere. It simply represents a brief summary of some of the important advances made during the past decade or so.

For many years the loudspeaker has been the most argued-over component in the entire hi fi chain, with every aspect of its design execution subject to lengthy and involved discussion. Although acoustic engineers like to deal in facts, much to their dismay, fashion plays a considerable part in the consumer stakes and loudspeakers are no exception to this rule. Occasionally an 'unbalanced' system will find public favour, such a model often being claimed to have a 'new sound', deriving from a different bass loading principle, or a new transducer and dispersion method. Unfortunately, other important aspects of its performance are likely to have been neglected by the designer in his efforts to incorporate this 'special' effect.

In the professional field, users are also inevitably conditioned by past experience and are often suspicious of any change, even for the better. Only those whose judgment is free of prejudice and who have frequent contact with live programme sources can reliably discuss reproduced sound quality.

Recently there has been an encouraging development, in that a degree of rationalisation of performance standards has occurred on both the domestic and professional fronts. The important designers are beginning to agree on a common standard of performance based on factors such as a natural frequency balance, uniformity of response and low distortion and colouration. This common ground has developed in spite of dissimilarities of design approach and philosophy, and it implies that sufficient objective and subjective data concerning speaker performance is at last becoming freely available.

Such a situation presents a dramatic reversal of the state of affairs prevailing some 15 years ago. A marked divergence of opinion then existed over subjective sound quality — indeed, this was so extreme that the products of the major manufacturers could be identified by a specific 'in-house' sound, which pervaded all their designs. A typical domes-

1

TABLE 1.1. IDEALISED LOUDSPEAKER SYSTEM SPECIFICATION, CIRCA 1965

Efficiency	100 dB at 1 m for 1 W at 100 Hz
Frequency response	100—10 000 Hz, ±4 dB; 35 Hz at −10 dB; 15 kHz at −10 dB
Polar response	100—10 000 Hz, less than 6 dB down at a 60° arc limit
Distortion	Less than 11% at 35 Hz, level unspecified
	Less than 2% at 100 Hz, level unspecified
	Less than 2% above 100 Hz
Cabinet volume	50 litres

TABLE 1.2. TYPICAL SPECIFICATION OF DOMESTIC TWO-WAY SYSTEM, CIRCA 1965

Efficiency	93 dB at 1 m for 1 W at 100 Hz
Frequency response	100 Hz to 10 000 Hz, ±6 dB
35 Hz limit	at −17 dB
15 kHz limit	at −12 dB
Polar response	Less than 6 dB down over a 60° arc, 100 Hz—5 kHz
Distortion	Above 200 Hz not quoted; at 100 Hz 4%, at 35 Hz, 10%
Power rating	25 W programme
Cabinet Volume	75 litres

tic 'hi fi' speaker system then comprised a 250 or 300 mm chassis diameter bass unit, with a light paper cone incorporating a 33 or 50 mm voice coil on a paper former. A separate paper-cone tweeter covered the treble range and was often concentrically mounted on the bass unit frame. The drivers were rear mounted on the inside face of the front panel, the enclosure was likely to have a typical volume of between 50 to 100 litres, and probably employ reflex loading.

It is interesting to examine the 'ideal performance' the contemporary speaker designer then aimed at achieving, even though the typical speaker, outlined above, in fact fell far short of this standard (Table 1.1).

The ideal specification was limited by the level of achievement currently attained by designers (Table 1.2 and Fig.1.1). Relative to the typical commercial system of the time. the ideal efficiency is placed at 100 dB for 1 W input at 1 m, which is 6 dB more sensitive than the typical specification. Presumably this difference reflects the relatively low power output of contemporary amplifiers as 10—20 W models were commonplace. Only a mild improvement in response flatness or bandwidth was then thought possible; the typical speaker gave a 35 Hz point at 17 dB down, and a 15 kHz point 12 dB down, which contrasts with the −10 dB limit of the ideal system.

[Handwritten annotations:]

Above "250": 10″ Above "300": 12″ Above "33": 1.5″ Above "50": 2″

1 L = 61 in³
50 L = 3050 in³ ≃ 1.8 cu ft
100 L = 6100 in³ ≃ 3.5 cu ft
1 cu ft = 1728 cu

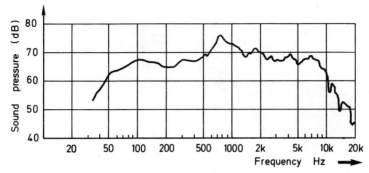

Figure 1.1   Typical response curve of two-way domestic system in Table 1.2

While it is important to view the specification in Table 1.2 in its proper context, that is as an example of typical contemporary commercial practice, it is surprising to discover that the basic technology and theory essential to good loudspeaker design was well known to advanced specialists in the field. Furthermore such work was well documented in many papers, periodicals and books; for example, although designers were aware of colouration effects they appear to have done little about them, despite the fine research that had been conducted almost twenty years earlier by Shorter at the BBC, concerning delayed resonances. Ten years ago much of the currently accepted loudspeaker technology and principles were rarely applied, and the overall approach to design was rather a haphazard exercise. However, some companies were researching highly advanced designs and a few were even in production, albeit in limited quantities. In 1967, K.E.F. Electronics (UK) released a costly experimental system incorporating a highly developed mid-band transducer. Covering a 250 Hz to 4 kHz range, this latter driver employed a 65 mm hemispherical dome formed in a rigid polystyrene/neoprene polymer, and was fitted with a double suspension and loaded by an 0.8 m pipe filled with long-fibre wool, for absorption. The use of an aluminium voice coil former resulted in a high power handling capacity (Fig.1.2).

At this time very few mid-range domes were available, the other well established example being that employed in the classic American design, the Acoustic Research AR3. One loudspeaker system that has survived the passage of the years virtually unscathed is the Quad full-range electrostatic loudspeaker. Accepting that moderate power handling and low efficiency are its specific limitations, its performance continues to bear favourable comparison with many current designs.

The conservative atmosphere then pervading the consumer market in the mid sixties may be judged from the following example. At that time the better class systems were relatively large, (50—100 litres)

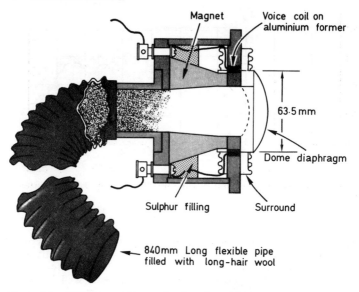

Figure 1.2   KEF's new mid-range loudspeaker with absorbent load

and when a new high performance model of compact dimensions became available, it was viewed with considerable suspicion. The Spendor BC1 (40 litres) sounded quite different to the systems currently available, and in fact was far nearer the live source in character than its contemporaries.

It represented a skilled balance of the important factors responsible for realistic sound quality, and yet it has taken almost a decade for this system to become widely accepted. Surprisingly enough, there are still quite a few so called 'high fidelity' speakers of the older generation still in production, their success actually based on their coloured sound characteristic, which although inaccurate, is apparently preferred by a significant number of purchasers.

By the mid 1960s, the BBC's work on a new generation of monitoring loudspeakers incorporating bextrene cones was well advanced. It proved to be of great significance as it was clear that a major improvement in loudspeaker quality had been achieved. The high standards set by these designs acted as a stimulus to the industry, and through attempts to attain this standard at a commercial level, many new developments and designs have appeared, some strongly related to the BBC originals.

The performance of today's typical high quality domestic systems would have been unbelievable in 1965, for they exceed the majority of requirements of the 1965 ideal specification by a handsome margin (Fig.1.3, Table 1.3).

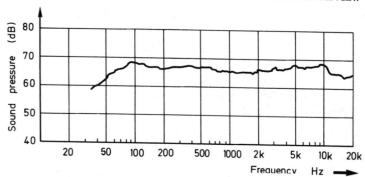

Figure 1.3 *Typical response curve of good quality two-way domestic system in Table 1.3*

TABLE 1.3. TYPICAL SPECIFICATION OF DOMESTIC TWO-WAY SYSTEM, CIRCA 1976

Efficiency	83 dB lin. at 100 Hz for 1 m, 1 W input
Frequency response	50 Hz to 18 kHz, ±3 dB; 35 Hz at −8 dB, −3 dB at 20 kHz
Polar response	Within ±3 dB of the axial curve over a 60° arc, 40 Hz to 15 kHz
Distortion	At 90 dB at 1 m: less than 0.5%, 100 Hz to 10 kHz; less than 5% at 35 Hz
Power rating	100 W programme
Cabinet volume	35 litres

This particular 1976 example is a bass reflex design, employing a plastic coned 20 cm bass-mid unit and a 2.5 cm plastic-dome treble unit. The great reduction in efficiency is a marked feature — nearly 20 dB below the proposed ideal for 1965. This is the inevitable outcome of the modern system's wide bandwidth in a compact enclosure, and its attainment of vastly lower subjective colouration. The narrower amplitude response limits is also important; simultaneously they contain a far greater response range, serving to illustrate the considerable improvement in uniformity and consistency of response. The standard achieved for distortion and polar response are both vastly improved, and the power rating of 100 W programme, (see Table 1.4) is 6 dB higher than the typical equivalent for 1965. This is the result of the reduced efficiency of the system as well as the considerably higher power ratings of recent transistor amplifiers. In the light of this current level of attainment and contemporary technology, the following is a suggested specification for a high performance loudspeaker of the mid 1970s.

TABLE 1.4. PROPOSED LOUDSPEAKER SPECIFICATION

Axial pressure response	100 Hz to 10 kHz, ±3 dB, (sine) 200 Hz to 5 kHz, ±1 dB, (octave averaged) 40 Hz at −3 dB, 20 kHz at −2 dB
Off axis response	±10° vertical within 3 dB of axial response ±30° lateral within 6 dB of axial response
Harmonic and inter- modulation distortion	at 90 dB sound pressure level (s.p.l.) 0.5%, 100 Hz to 10 kHz <5%, 50 Hz to 100 Hz <10% below 50 Hz
Sensitivity/efficiency	90 dB lin for 1 W, at 1 metre, anechoic
Power rating	100 W or more programme rating. (Equivalent to the output of a 100 W continuous rated amplifier driven on normal programme signals, rather than a laboratory sine wave or similar continuous inputs)
Impedance	8 Ω nominal, 6 < Z < 20 Ω; phase angle of impedance not greater than 30° over 100 Hz to 10 kHz
Maximum pressure level	Domestic: 105 dB lin at 1 m Monitoring: 115 dB lin at 1 m Stage amplification: 125 dB lin at 1 m
Size (ideal)	Domestic: 25–50 l Monitoring: 50–100 l Stage amplification: 75–150 l

The recent improvement in quality is not confined only to the high performance end of the market: in fact all loudspeaker systems have advanced similarly if not equally over the same period. For example, many of the causes of colouration in both cabinets and drive units have been identified and can now be adequately suppressed. Further key factors concern a refined understanding of diaphragm behaviour, with the successful application of synthetic materials to drive-unit manufacture. A sufficient variety of well designed drivers are now available, which cover specific sections of the audio spectrum over a range of different power levels and allow the designer considerable latitude when determining the size and cost factors for a given system. A key unit in success of a number of the original BBC and subsequent design derviatives is the Celestion high frequency unit, the HF1300 series. Designed around 1957, it is suitable for medium power applications and was first used by GEC with their aluminium cone drivers. Some twenty years later it is still a popular unit and is employed in many of today's high performance systems. It was primarily based on a pressure unit for a high frequency horn, and was later modified for use as a direct radiator, notably by the addition of the phase correcting front plate.

However there still remains a major problem for drive unit manufacturers, namely suitable cone materials. Bextrene has proved highly successful for the manufacture of vacuum formed cones and has gained wide acceptance among the major UK drive unit/speaker manufactures, although it was almost a chance discovery, as the material was originally designed for use in the production of low-cost moulded packaging. However, in the more critical loudspeaker application, experienced drive unit manufacturers have discovered that Bextrene's acoustical and mechanical properties can show variations from batch to batch. The chemical industry is not particularly interested in solving these problems as the requirements are small compared with total sales. It is thus essential to carefully quantify the mechanical properties of the material to be used and to continue to do so for each batch ordered. Despite these technical difficulties, with careful design and manufacture, plastic cones can be greatly superior to pulp/paper composition types in colouration, uniformity of response and sample-to-sample consistency. Currently, certain speaker companies are working on new plastics that not only offer improved acoustic properties by comparison with bextrene, but have the added benefit of a simple and more repeatable chemical formula.

Concerning the response irregularities, the fundamental analysis of loudspeakers at low frequencies conducted by Thiele, and first presented in 1961, has been recognised for its true worth in recent years, and the subsequent research on the subject by Small has also proved of great value to designers. Papers by these and other authors provide a remarkably complete theoretical analysis of the one area of loudspeaker design where the results are highly predictable. (A summary of this work is given in Chapter 4.) Armed with such theory there is no reason why any loudspeaker designer worthy of note should fail to produce a loudspeaker with a less than optimal low frequency characteristic.

Refined electronic crossover techniques are responsible for further improvements to the modern generation of loudspeaker designs. Although the idea is not new, the early active filters were clumsy to execute with valve amplification and found little favour. In recent years the development of active-filter theory and inexpensive operational amplifier circuit modules, together with the low cost of transistor power amplifier units, has given renewed impetus and several active designs have been produced, including some for domestic use. It is to be expected that such designs will eventually take over the high performance end of the market, although this may take several years to effect.

As to the future, we can only hope that through the application of both extant and future research material, loudspeaker designers will continue to support the common standard of performance that is beginning to emerge today. No car would find acceptance if it failed to meet basic requirements of handling, braking efficiency, acceleration and comfort, yet the existence of such standards has not prevented the automobile industry from producing a wide range of models of diverse style and size. Similarly, there is no reason why an interesting range of speakers should not continue to be available, while aiming to meet or exceed a common standard of bandwidth, response uniformity, colouration and distortion.

BIBLIOGRAPHY

Briggs, G. *Loudspeakers*, 5th edn, Wharfedale Wireless Works, Idle, Yorkshire (1958)
Briggs, G. *More About Loudspeakers*, Wharfedale Wireless Works, Idle, Yorkshire (1963)
Cohen, A. B. *Hi Fi Loudspeakers and Enclosures*, (1975)
Jordan, E. J. *Loudspeakers*, Focal Press, London (1963)
Rice, C. W. and Kellogg, E. W. 'Notes on the development of a new type of horn-less loudspeaker', *J.A.I.E.E.*
Tremaine, H. M. *Audio Cyclopedia*, 2nd edn, Howard Sams, New York (1974)

2

Theoretical aspects of diaphragm radiators

This chapter contains a brief review of those factors which control the behaviour of loudspeaker drivers. (Acoustic loading, particularly at low frequencies, is dealt with in Chapter 4.) Numerous technical works are currently available which cover this field, but they require a good working knowledge of acoustics, mathematics and physics. Although such a background is essential to a thorough understanding of the subject, it is often sufficient for a loudspeaker engineer to be aware of the basic theory rather than delving too deeply into acoustic principles.

2.1 DIAPHRAGM OR PISTON

Except for ionic and flame type transducers, all drive units possess some sort of vibrating diaphragm, although the way in which this is energised may vary considerably. The diaphragm may be one of a variety of shapes, a cone, a flat surface or piston, a dome, etc. Its method of suspension or support can also vary from none at all, to a separate half-roll or multi-roll structure.

Over the frequency range where the diaphragm moves as a whole, without breakup, it can be equated to a rigid piston. Furthermore, the shape is relatively unimportant as it has little effect on the medium frequency radiation properties which are the concern of this chapter. (The shape or profile is dictated by considerations of material strength, among other factors, and strongly influences the location of the breakup frequencies.)

The behaviour of a circular, rigid piston is well defined, and is essentially derived from the fundamental work of Lord Kelvin, the Victorian physicist.

Several situations are pertinent, and are illustrated below.

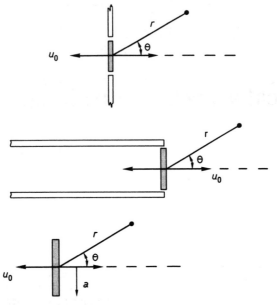

Figure 2.1   Circular piston in three important mounting conditions: (a) infinite baffle, (b) on face of long cylinder, (c) in free space

Derivation of sound pressure at a given point due to vibrating piston

The analysis involves the division of the piston surface into small elements, vibrating in phase. The sound pressure at a given point, distance r from the piston, at any angle θ is formed by summing the contributions from the individual components through mathematical integration. For example the resulting equation for sound pressure from Fig. 2.1 (a) is

$$P = \frac{\sqrt{2}j\rho_0 U_0 \pi a^2}{r} \left(\frac{2J_1(ka \sin \theta)}{ka \sin \theta} \right) e^{j\omega(t-r/c)} \qquad (2.1)$$

where ρ_0 = the density of the gas, i.e. that of air in kg/m^3; c = speed of sound in metres per second, i.e. 345 m/s at $20°C$; J_1 = a Bessel function, where

$$J_1(x) = \frac{x}{2} - \frac{x^3}{2^2 \cdot 4} + \frac{x^5}{2^2 \cdot 4^2 \cdot 6} - \frac{x^7}{2^2 \cdot 4^2 \cdot 6^2 \cdot 8} \cdots$$

a = piston radius (metres); λ = wavelength of sound in air (metres);

$k = \omega/c$ or $= 2\pi/\lambda$, the wave number; U_0 = piston velocity in metres per second.

Directivity

The ratio of sound pressure P_θ at an angle θ degrees off-axis to the on-axis pressure P_0 at the same distance is

$$\frac{P_\theta}{P_0} = 1 - \frac{2\pi a (\sin\theta)}{8\,\lambda}$$

or

$$\frac{P_\theta}{P_0} = 1 - \frac{ka\sin\theta}{8}$$

where

$$ka = \frac{\text{circumference of piston}}{\text{emitted wavelength}}$$

The directivity index is defined as

$$\text{DI} = 10\log_{10}\left(\frac{P_\theta}{P_0}\right)$$

Directional or beaming properties

Taking Fig.2.1a at low frequencies, a vibrating piston of radius a, which is small by comparison with the emitted wavelength, has a radiating pattern essentially that of a hemisphere (Fig.2.2a) with half the total power radiated on each side of the baffle. Hence the directivity index is equal to 3 dB as the baffle is 'infinite', and only the frontal radiation is available. This case is true in principle for any driver, mounted in a large baffle, from a cone bass to a dome treble unit.

Two practical points are of interest here. When a driver is mounted in a sealed box which approximates to an infinite baffle, the front baffle size is necessarily finite. Below the frequency at which the baffle dimensions approximate to a sound wavelength, the radiation begins to revert to an omnidirectional or spherical pattern. With increasing wavelength the sound energy diffracts around the box (Fig.2.3d).

Other factors can also influence directivity. Departure from piston operation is usual at higher frequencies, resulting in areas of the diaphragm vibrating out of phase with the main drive, with consequent

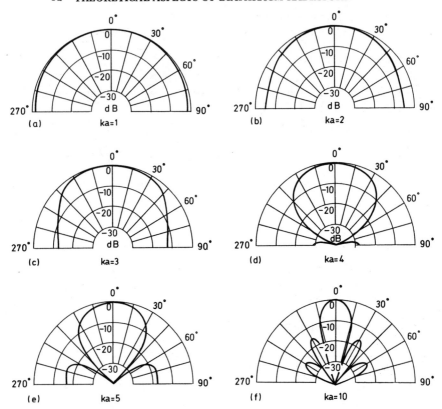

Figure 2.2   Directivity patterns for a rigid circular piston in an infinite baffle as a function of ka = 2πa/λ, *where* a *is the radius of the piston (after Beranek)*

amplitude and directivity irregularities. A designer may also employ short horn or plate structures to control the directivity over a specific range.

The velocity of sound in the diaphragm may be another complication with the larger units when used at higher frequencies. It has been suggested that in units where the velocity in the diaphragm is greatly different to that in air, the differential component results in a mismatch at the diaphragm/air interface which may result in phase cancellation at certain frequencies.

Figure 2.1b will apply to baffled drivers where the box is deep and the front panel area barely greater than the driver diaphragm; for example, a column enclosure or a compact system with a large LF driver. The directivity is obtained by analysing the combined effects of the piston area and the diffraction which occurs at the enclosure edges. As

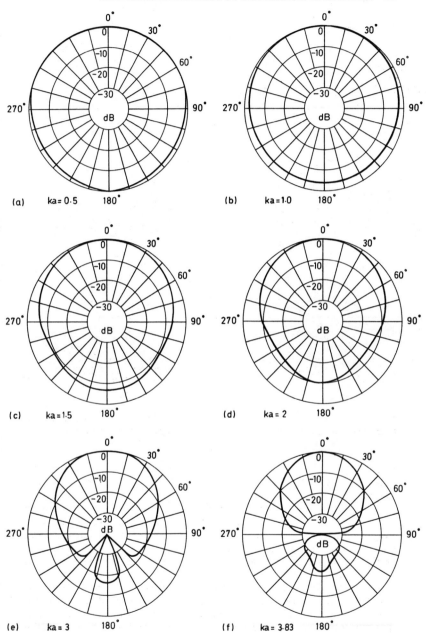

Figure 2.3   Directivity patterns for a rigid circular piston in the end of a long tube as a function of ka = $2\pi/\lambda$, *where* a *is the radius of the piston (after Beranek)*

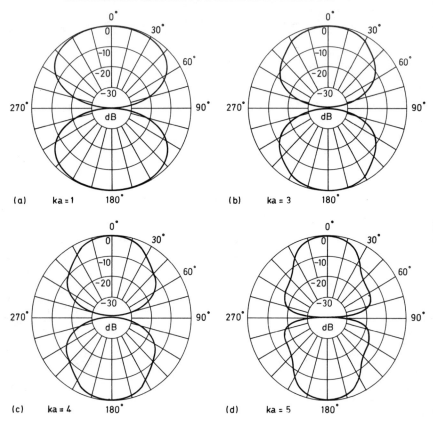

Figure 2.4   Directivity patterns for an unbaffled rigid circular piston of radius a located in free space at an angle θ a large distance r from the point of measurement. For ka<1, the directivity pattern is the same as that for the doublet

with the other two cases, the directivity diagram in this instance is only valid for far field where the distance r is large compared with the piston radius (Fig.2.3).

Finally we come to the unbaffled piston, which although less common than the first two cases, is nonetheless important, Fig.2.4. Most open backed electrostatic or magnetic drive thin-film diaphragms belong to this group.

Control of directivity

For any piston radiator, the directivity is dependent on the frequency of the sound radiated. The audible frequency range spans nine octaves, with an accompanying range of wavelength from 11 m to 2 cm. From directivity considerations alone, such a range is beyond the compass of a single driver, irrespective of the practical problems of design and assembly (see p.45)

For this reason any high quality system will contain several drivers of graded size, which allow a uniform directivity to be maintained over the frequency range. In general one driver should be crossed over to a smaller unit when the diameter of the former is equivalent to one wavelength.

Where narrow directional qualities are required, for example to project a sound field to specific regions of a large audience, converse design may be used. Arrays can be built where the radiating properties of sources which are large compared with the emitted sound wavelength are deliberately exploited and the crossover points are then chosen to maintain the effect over the required bandwidth. Horn systems are naturally more directional than simple radiators and are widely used in this application, especially with sub divisions or 'multi-cells' which maintain the required radiation pattern to higher frequencies.

2.2 PISTON RADIATING ACOUSTIC POWER

So far we have considered directivity, which is a function of frequency, driver size and baffle type, but the sound pressure developed at a distance by a diaphragm is also dependent on other factors such as the air loading. The following brief look at diaphragm radiation behaviour mainly concerns the axial response, and the directivity effects so far discussed may be combined with these to give the total picture.

Equations have been established for the mechanical impedance of the air load presented to a piston, those reproduced here applying to an infinite flat baffle[1].

Z_{MA} (mechanical impedance of air load) =

$= R_{MA}$ (resistive or real part) $+ jX_{MA}$ (reactive or imaginary part)

or

$$Z_{MA} = \pi a^2 \rho_0 c \left[1 - \frac{J_1(2ka)}{ka} \right] + \frac{j\pi\rho_0 c}{2k^2} K_1(2ka) \qquad (2.2)$$

where Z_{MA} is in Ns/m or mechanical ohms, and R_{MA} = mechanical resistance in ohms. J_1, K_1 are the respective appropriate Bessell functions which may be represented by the series

$$J_1(\dot{x}) = \frac{x}{2} - \frac{x^3}{2^2 \cdot 4} + \frac{x^5}{2^2 \cdot 4^2 \cdot 6} - \frac{x^7}{2^2 \cdot 4^2 \cdot 6^2 \cdot 8} \cdots$$

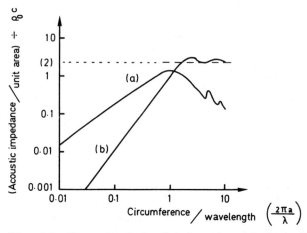

Figure 2.5   Mass and radiation impedance curves for both sides of a circular piston with an infinite baffle where (a) is the normalised curve due to air mass $(X_{MA}/\pi a^2 \rho_0 c)$ *and (b) is the normalised resistance curve* $(R_{MA} = \pi a^2 \rho_0 c)$

$$K_1(x) = 2\left[\frac{x^3}{3} - \frac{x^5}{3^2 \cdot 5} + \frac{x^7}{3^2 \cdot 5^2 \cdot 7} \cdots\right]$$

where $x = 2ka$.

For most work the acoustic impedance equation 2.2 may be greatly simplified by utilising only the early terms of the Bessel series, and this form will be utilised for later sections of this chapter[2]. At low frequencies where $ka \ll 2$, the first two terms of the $J_1(x)$, $K_1(x)$ series are sufficient which leaves

$$Z_{MA(LF)} \simeq \tfrac{1}{2}\rho_0 ck^2 \pi a^4 + j\frac{8}{3}\rho_0 cka^3 \tag{2.3}$$

At high frequencies where $ka \gg 2$, only the first terms are required, so

$$Z_{MA(HF)} \simeq \rho c\pi a^2 + j\frac{2}{k}\rho ca \tag{2.4}$$

Inspection of the acoustic impedance curves (Figs.2.5 and 2.6) shows that at low frequencies, where ka is considerably less than 2, (1 is the approximate threshold) the mass or reactive component is dominant, whereas at higher frequencies, where ka is much greater than 2, (3 being the approximate threshold) the total acoustic impedance is primarily resistive at 42 Ω and is relatively constant.

It is worth examining the influence of these effects on the radiated power. In order to do this, our massless, resonance-free piston must be energised sinusoidally, by a force F. The air load on both faces must be

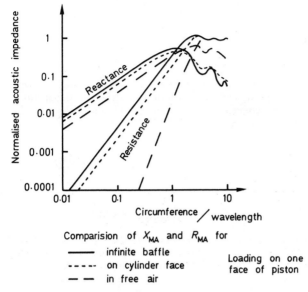

Figure 2.6

driven, despite the fact that the rear radiation is unused in an infinite baffle. The piston velocity U is given by the following equation, where

$$U = \frac{F}{2Z_{MA}}$$

If the driving force is assumed constant with frequency, the radiated power equals $U^2 \times R_{MA}$, and the radiated power usefully available is thus

$$P = \frac{F^2}{Z_{MA}^2} \cdot R_{MA} \text{ (from one side)}$$

If the above approximations concerning the dominance of X_{MA} at low frequencies and R_{MA} at high frequencies are employed, then separate relationships may be obtained for the radiated power under the two conditions. These are as follows:

$$P_{LF} = \frac{F^2}{R_{LF}}$$

and

$$P_{HF} = \frac{F^2 R_{HF}}{X_{HF}^2}$$

Over both these regions the sound pressure is level, (this includes real cases such as the magnetic and electrostatic film driven designs) but a step in power occurs between the two. This is obvious if the ratio of the two power relations is considered.

$$\frac{P_{LF}}{P_{HF}} = \frac{X_{HF}^2}{R_{HF} R_{LF}}$$

Substitution of normalised values taken from the graph in Fig.2.5 gives P_{LF}/P_{HF} = 2, i.e. the power step is 3 dB (6 dB in sound pressure) between the high frequency and low frequency ranges.

The piston will become more directional at higher frequencies where ka is greater than 3, and will cause the available power to increasingly concentrate on the following axis with rising frequency, and in consequence the axial pressure will also increase. At lower frequencies, where ka is less than 1, the radiation is virtually hemispherical and the axial and off-axis pressure will be approximately equal.

Thus it is possible for a diaphragm in a finite sealed box baffle to have two 'steps' in its axial pressure response, the first occurring at the frequency where the enclosure becomes an obstacle to the propagated sound wave, and the second where the diaphragm circumference/wavelength (ka) approximates to a numerical value of 2. With a large bass unit mounted in a small enclosure these two frequencies may be fairly close together, the +6 dB cabinet dimension 'lift' partially compensating for the −6 dB fall which is due to the radiation impedance transition. (The moving coil driver exhibits a further fall above ka = 2, which will be discussed later.)

However in practice this above possibility is remote, as real drivers possess mass, suspension stiffness and accompanying losses or mechanical resistance. In addition there must be a 'motor' or translation mechanism to produce a mechanical force from an electrical drive. These factors complicate the issue.

A small digression is essential at this point in order to introduce the equivalent circuit of a moving coil motor system.

2.3 A HYPOTHETICAL MOVING-COIL DIRECT RADIATOR

So far the discussion has been confined to an imaginary piston with no mass or resonances whatever. In practice however a drive unit will possess a diaphragm and accompanying moving system of Mass = M_D, a suspension or flexible support of compliance C_{MS}, and a mechanical

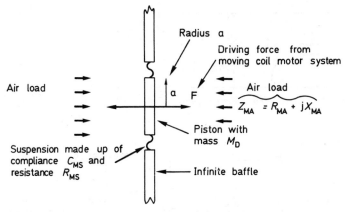

Figure 2.7   Moving coil energised piston in infinite baffle (showing mass, stiffness and resistance)

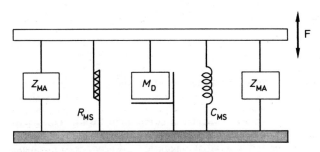

Figure 2.8   Mechanical circuit of Figure 2.7

resistance R_{MS}, Figs.2.7 and 2.8. We shall ignore for the moment the other components of the motor section — magnet, voice coil etc.

While Fig.2.8 shows a mechanical diagram, this system may be represented by electrical components where mass becomes capacitance, and inductance represents compliance, the resulting mechanico—electrical circuit represented by Fig.2.9 (see Fig.5.1).

The worth of the electrical equivalent lies in the ease with which standard electrical circuit theory may be applied to analyse what would otherwise be a difficult acoustical problem. We shall now include the moving coil components comprising the coil d.c. resistance R_C, inductance L_C and mass M_C (the latter is included in the total moving mass M_D) which are incorporated in the equivalent circuit, resulting in Fig.2.10, this also included the 'source' or generator components, resistance R_g and voltage E (see Fig.3.21).

Figure 2.10 includes a transiormation step between the electrical and

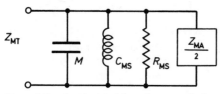

Figure 2.9   An electrical impedance equivalent circuit of Figure 2.8

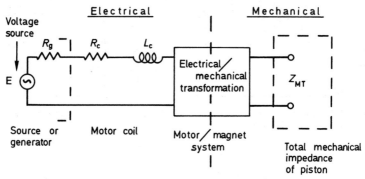

Figure 2.10   Electrical circuit including generator and coil

the mechanical parts, (albeit in electrical component form). This transformation derives from the motor principle whereby an electric current flowing in a coil immersed in a radial magnetic field produces a mechanical force in the coil along its axis.

The factors are flux density B, the coil wire length l actually immersed in the magnet flux, and the current in the coil, I. For a unit current, $F = Bl$, and hence the transformer may be represented by Fig.2.11.

Transformer theory gives the relation

$$\frac{I}{F} \propto \left(\frac{n_1}{n_2}\right)^2$$

hence

$$\frac{I}{F} \propto (Bl)^2$$

The electrical quantities may be transferred via the 'motor transformer' to the mechanical side utilising the $(Bl)^2$ constant where their combined effects may be assessed. This complete mechanically based electric

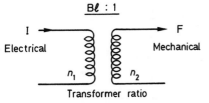

Figure 2.11   The 'motor transformer'

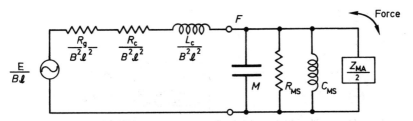

Figure 2.12   Electrical parts referred via 'transformer' to mechanical side (represented in mobility form)

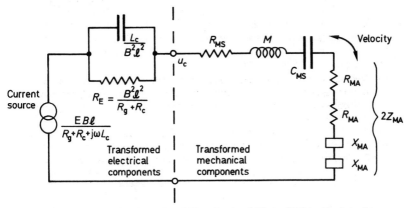

Figure 2.13   Transformation of mobility circuit of Figure 2.12 to the impedance or velocity form. In this circuit, F, the driving force, is transformed into Uc, the piston or coil velocity, which is equivalent to a voltage or pressure in a conventional electric circuit

circuit, shown in Fig.2.12, which in mechanical terms is referred to as a mobility arrangement, may be rearranged into the equivalent impedance form of Fig.2.13, for ease of analysis. In this latter form the mechanical circuit can be subjected to rigorous mathematical analysis but for the purposes of this chapter it is sufficient to simplify its treatment by examining convenient divisions.

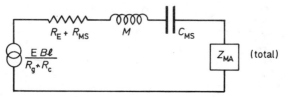

Figure 2.14   Simplified circuit of Figure 2.13 at medium to low frequencies (Region A and B of Figure 2.18)

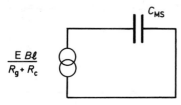

Figure 2.15   Simplified circuit of Figure 2.14 at very low frequencies (Region A of Fig.2.18)

In the circuit of Fig.2.13, at the junction between the electrical and mechanical sections, we have the voice coil velocity U_c, which is directly related to the driver excursion, and thus controls the output power and hence the sound pressure level.

The circuit of Fig.2.13 provides the foundation for the analysis. For example, at medium to low frequencies L_c is negligible, leaving the simplified circuit as shown in Fig.2.14.

This represents a simple LC resonant system with air loading Z_{MA} and damping $R_e + R_c$, which possesses the universal resonance curve for U_c, the coil velocity. If we assume for the moment that the directivity of this hypothetical driver is constant over the frequency range, then the sound pressure and coil velocity will follow the same variation as that for a simple resonance circuit, (a plot of current against normalised frequency for a series RLC circuit).

In decibel form, this curve gives slopes on either side of the peak tending to 6 dB/octave. When the velocity is translated into sound pressure, or acoustic power, and plotted against frequency, the additional linear frequency term tilts the curve, so that below resonance, the roll off approaches 12 dB per octave (6 + 6 dB), and above resonance is actually flat, (−6 + 6 dB = 0 dB). (This follows from the acoustic power relation, $P \propto f U_c^2$).

Region A of Fig.2.18

Figure 2.15 is a simplification of Fig.2.14 which is valid at very low

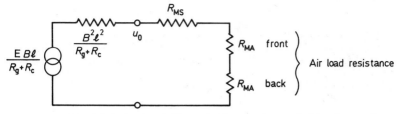

Figure 2.16 Simplified circuit of Figure 2.14 at resonance f_0 *(reactive components disappear) (Region B)*

frequencies. At very low frequencies C_{MS} is dominant, and the other components such as the air load are negligible. The output is proportional to the fourth power of frequency, which implies a fall of 12 dB/octave with reducing frequency below the fundamental resonance $(P \propto f^2 . f^2 C_{MS})$

Region B of Fig.2.18

Figure 2.16 shows the components of Fig.2.14 which are relevant at resonance, a condition where the reactive parts cancel leaving resistive effects only.

At resonance L_C is still negligible; L and C disappear as the velocity/power is wholly resistive and X_{MA} is zero. The output at resonance is thus dependent on the total resistance, including that of the generator or source R_g. This figure shows that as R_g is increased the losses are reduced; that is, Q is inversely proportional to R_g. This is the reverse of what might be expected, and the source resistance can be seen to be an important damping element in the fundamental resonance of the system.

The coil resistance is the other major factor as, in practice, the suspension losses are usually low. If R_g is large or $B^2 l^2$ small, the Q can exceed unity and thus develop a peak in the sound output. This will be covered in greater detail in the chapters on LF loading (Chapters 3 and 4).

Region C of Fig.2.18

Above resonance, (Fig.2.17) at medium frequencies, the radiation is still essentially hemispherical so that the directivity is constant, and the sound pressure and power output are directly related. It is possible for a driver to have a level output in this range, as the frequency squared term in the radiation resistance R_{MA} is nullified by the frequency squared term in the mass reactance, (piston and air mass load). This condition is known as 'mass controlled', resulting in a constant output over this range. It assumes that the resistive components R_{MS} etc., are small; if not, the resonance may be overdamped, 'rounding the corner' and tilting

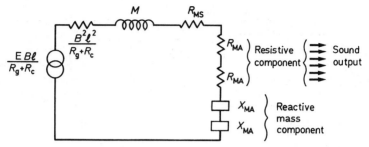

Figure 2.17 Simplified circuit of Figure 2.13 above resonance, medium frequencies (Region C)

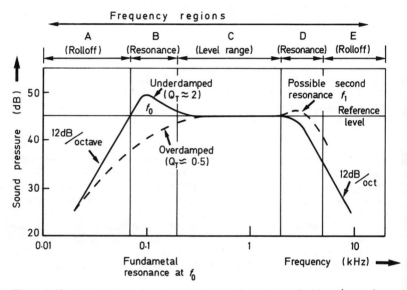

Figure 2.18 Fundamental bandpass response of moving coil driver (over the range where directivity may be assumed constant, sound pressure and power may be shown by the same curve)

the flat region to some degree. (This is represented by the dotted area in Fig.2.18.) Excessive Bl will also reduce the span of this region through overdamping.

Region D of Fig.2.18

At higher frequencies, a second resonance is theoretically possible. Inspection of Fig.2.13 shows that the coil inductance can become sig-

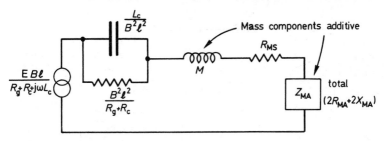

Figure 2.19 *High-frequency equivalent circuit of Figure 2.14 (resonances involving summed masses and L_c/B^2l^2) (Region D)*

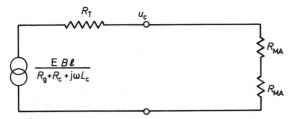

Figure 2.20 *Simplified circuit of Figure 2.19 at resonance (Region D). Total resistance*

$$R_T = \frac{(R_g + R_c)B^2l^2}{(R_g + R_c)^2 + \omega^2 L_c^2}$$

nificant at higher frequencies, (as represented by the capacitor in our impedance equivalent circuit) and it may resonate with the mass component remaining in the loop, this network given in Fig.2.19.

At resonance only the resistive components apply, as seen in Fig.2.20. The resonant frequency is given by

$$\frac{\omega L_c B^2 l^2}{\omega^2 L_c^2 + (R_g + R_c)^2} = \omega M + 2X_{MA}$$

Interestingly enough, if $(R_g + R_c)^2$ is large compared with $L_c^2 \omega^2$, the parallel combination of L_C/B^2l^2 with $B^2l^2/(R_g + R_c)$ produces a negative inductance, $-B^2l^2 L_c/(R_g + R_c)^2$, and no resonance lift will occur.

Region E of Fig.2.18

At very high frequencies, above second resonance, we reach the upper range where the acoustic resistance is virtually constant and is thus independent of frequency, while the acoustic mass contribution has fallen to negligible proportions (see Fig.2.5).

The simplified circuit in Fig.2.21 is now dominated by only two

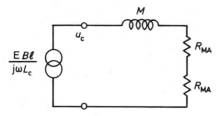

Figure 2.21 Simplified circuit at very high frequencies, i.e. above second resonance (Region E). The coil inductance, L_c is dominant and R_{MA} is constant at $\rho_0 c \pi a^2$

components; the constant radiation resistance and the mass reactance of the moving piston itself, (including motor coil, etc.). The normal 6 dB/octave rolloff for this single-pole filter is modified by the linear frequency term, producing a final rolloff (of 12 dB/octave) after second resonance.

Inspection of the pressure response (Fig.2.18) shows that the most uniformly wide characteristic is obtained if the fundamental resonance is optimally damped and the compliance is high, giving a low resonant frequency. This is the theory underlying the widespread use of small, high compliance bass/mid drivers.

2.4 DEVELOPMENT OF THE AXIAL SOUND PRESSURE

The preceding analysis assumed a constant hemispherical directivity and pure piston operation. It is now necessary to apply further factors such as directivity variation and diaphragm breakup in order to develop a theoretical basis for the axial sound pressure as produced by a practical drive unit.

Initially we will consider the case of an infinite baffle mounted driver radiating into a half-space (hemisphere or 2π steradians). This condition is approximated by a wall-mounted, flush-fitted box system or more simply, a wall-mounted driver. The sound pressure will follow the power curve (Fig.2.18) until the diaphragm diameter is comparable with the wavelength of sound in air.

If we begin at Region C, the level power range in Fig.2.18, both power and axial pressure response are uniform at low frequencies. With increasing frequency a point is reached where the diaphragm begins to concentrate sound pressure on axis, and the sound pressure will in consequence rise with increasing frequency. Reference to the section on directivity shows that when the ka approaches unity, that is the piston circumference approximates to one wavelength, the piston becomes increasingly directional. The axial gain which may be expressed as Q, the directivity factor, approaches 6 dB/octave.

It so happens that the hazy division between the regions C and D of the power curve (Fig.2.18) lies between *ka* values of 1 and 2. If the second resonance is overdamped, the directivity gain may offer some compensation, which will then result in a response extension with certain diaphragms. The 12 dB rolloff beyond second resonance will now tend to a 6 dB/octave slope, due to the narrowing directivity. This is by no means coincidental, as the equations for directivity are derived from the same acoustic effects as the radiation impedance.

For example, consider a 200 mm diameter driver chassis with a well behaved cone. If we take *ka* = 2 as the upper limit of the level region, the transition point from hemispherical to forward radiation is given by

$$f_t \simeq \frac{C}{2\pi a} \simeq \frac{345}{2\pi \times 0.09} \simeq 1.2 \text{ kHz}$$

where 0.09 m = nominal piston radius.

The sound pressure is likely to be reasonably maintained for an octave beyond 1.2 kHz, above which the sound output should fall by 6 dB per octave.

In practice, most cone diaphragms enter the first major breakup mode or departure from true piston behaviour at values of *ka* between 1 and 2, with the poorer examples producing audible breakup effects at half that frequency. When a cone is in breakup, the theory described above is of little value, as the air load impedance and moving mass will be indeterminate, according to the specific breakup mode present at each frequency. This behaviour will be discussed in more detail in the later section on cones.

Reference efficiency

The level region for a moving coil driver provides a reference for the calculation of power output and efficiency[1]. It also gives a starting point for a system designer to match to the power level of drivers covering other sections of the range. The reference power available efficiency is given by·

$$P_{ref} = \frac{800 R_g . B^2 l^2 . \rho_0 . \pi^2 a^4}{2\pi c (R_g + R_c)^2 \times (M_D + M_A)^2} \% \qquad (2.5)$$

or in more typical form using $S_D^2 = \pi^2 a^4$

$$P_{ref} = \frac{\rho_0}{2\pi c} . \frac{B^2 l^2 S_D^2}{(M_D + M_A)^2} . \frac{800 R_g}{(R_g + R_c)} \% \qquad (2.6)$$

Equation 2.6 applies to the total output from both sides of the cone where the unusual condition of electrical power matching from a significant generator resistance R_g is included. In practice R_g tends to zero with low output impedance amplifiers and the above equation then makes little sense.

Taking an efficiency criterion based on power input versus power out, the reference efficiency is

$$\eta_0 = \frac{\rho_0}{2\pi c} \cdot \frac{B^2 l^2 . S_D^2}{(M_D + M_A)^2} \cdot \frac{200}{R_c} \% \tag{2.7}$$

Comparing Equation 2.7 with 2.6 it may be seen that if the optimum power transfer condition is allowed, ie. $R_g = R_c$ then the two agree. For one side, as is usual for a box enclosure, the value in Equation 2.7 should be halved.

It can be shown that

$$\eta_0 = 100 \cdot \frac{4\pi^2}{c^3} \cdot \frac{f_0^3 V_{AS}}{Q_E} \tag{2.8}$$

or with substitution for the constants,

$$\eta_0 = 9.6 \times 10^{-6} \cdot \frac{f_0^3 V_{AS}}{Q_E} \%$$

For the driver described in Fig.8.31

$$\eta_0 = 0.4\% \qquad \text{(with } Q_E = 0.5\text{)}$$

for the available output, which is a low value, and illustrates the inefficiency of small 'long-throw' low-colouration drivers.

From Equation 2.7 we see that the total mass term is squared. For the above driver size

$$M_A = \frac{8\rho_0 a^3}{3} = \frac{8 \times 1.18 \times 0.086^3}{3} \text{ kg} = 2 \text{ g per side}$$

which implies that the cone mass is 16 g, which is large for a 200 mm frame unit. If a pulp cone of possibly poorer colouration were substituted and the compliance adjusted to maintain the resonance frequency, the mass might be halved to 8 g giving a total of 12 g which would result in a power output improvement of nearly three times giving an $\eta_0 = 1.1\%$

Sensitivity and efficiency

It should not be forgotten that such a change in moving mass will have other consequences such as a relative increase in electrical damping at the fundamental resonance and thus a major change in the low frequency response.   In the reference frequency region where the sound radiation from a system is omnidirectional or hemispherical in the case of an infinite baffle, the s.p.l. at a given distance is proportional to the square root of the radiated total acoustic power. Assuming a nominally fixed electrical input resistance which is dominated by R_c the electrical power input is proportional to the square of the voltage applied. This is the basis for Equation 2.7 for η_0.

In practice the concept of efficiency is not much used in loudspeaker design and measurement except on a theoretical basis. Accepting that the source resistance is low for both leads and amplifier, it is usual to specify the sensitivity of a loudspeaker for a given voltage input – usually 2.83 V which produces 1 W into a nominal 8 Ω standard load.   Thus a specification for the example unit would read, 'sensitivity = 84 dB/W at 1 m'.

While the concept of efficiency has some relevance in the case of a single drive unit operating in the reference piston range it becomes meaningless in the context of a complex multi unit loudspeaker system. Factors such as the variable and reactive input impedance and variable directivity exhibited by such systems over their working frequency ranges makes a power in/power out relation unusable.

A method which can be used, though probably of limited significance, consists of driving a speaker system in a reverberant chamber with random noise excitation.   The power input is assessed by monitoring the full bandwidth integrated value of the voltage and current input, and the acoustic output from the integrated sound power assessed from measurement of the reverberant field.

REFERENCES

1. Beranek, L., *Acoustics*, McGraw-Hill, London (1954)
2. Jordan, E. J., *Loudspeakers*, Focal Press, London (1963)
3. Small, R. H., 'Direct radiator loudspeaker system analysis', *J. Audio Engng Soc.*, **20**, No.5 (1972)

BIBLIOGRAPHY

Bauer, B. B., 'Equivalent circuit analysis of mechano-acoustic structures', *J. Audio Engng. Soc.*, **24**, No.8, 643–655 (1976)
Gayford, M. L., *Acoustical Techniques And Transducers*, Macdonald & Evans London (1961)

Kelly, S., 'Loudspeaker enclosure survey', *Wireless World,* 552—8, November (1972)

Olsen, H. F., *Modern Sound Reproduction,* Van Nostrand, New York (1972)

Rettinger, M., *Practical Electroacoustics,* Thames and Hudson, London (1955)

Walker, P. J., 'Wide-range electrostatic loudspeakers', *Wireless World,* May, June and August (1955)

Walker, P. J., 'New developments in electrostatic loudspeakers', *Audio Engng Soc. 63rd Convention Preprint* 1472 (D-10) (1979)

3

The performance of practical diaphragms

So far we have examined a hypothetical diaphragm — a flat infinitely rigid piston. This is a reasonable approximation for high performance drivers, from the very lowest frequencies to the reference level range. For example, a good quality 300 mm chassis size driver should still approximate to a piston up to 500 Hz; a 200 mm cone driver to 1 kHz and a 25 mm rigid dome unit to 10 kHz, or possibly beyond. While such operation is generally valid with regard to the uniformity of sound pressure response, colouration due to suppressed resonances within this working range may still be audible.

The factors responsible for departures from pure piston performance may be divided into two interdependent categories; firstly, those due to geometry, i.e. the diaphragm shape, and secondly, those resulting from the mechanical properties of the chosen diaphragm material.

3.1 DOME RADIATORS

Phase loss

A dome made from our hypothetical, perfect material will have a series of dips or nulls in its pressure response on the axis, at frequencies where the path difference between the apex and the rim is a multiple of a half-wavelength of that frequency in air. A phase difference exists near these nulls which causes the axial output to fall gently towards the null, this phenomenon is termed 'phase loss[1,2] (Figs.3.1 and 3.2).

The frequency f_1 at which the dip occurs is dependent on h, the dome height. A shallow profile will place f_1 high.

For example, in a typical 25 mm doped fabric dome, h is commonly around 7.5 mm.

$$f = \frac{c}{\lambda} = \frac{345 \text{ m/s}}{7.5 \text{ mm}} = 46 \text{ kHz}$$

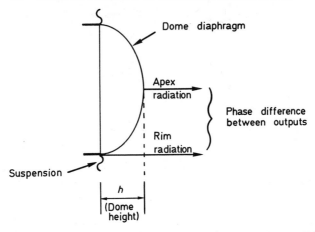

Figure 3.1   Dome geometry and phase loss (first dip when λ = 2h)

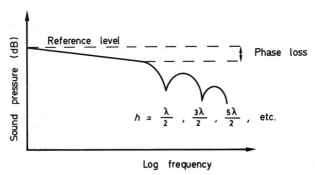

Figure 3.2   Typical dome response dominated by phase loss

and the first dip occurs at λ/2, that is at 23 kHz.

A smaller 19 mm diameter thermoplastic diaphragm of h typically 3.75 mm, will possess a first null at 46 kHz, well above audibility. However with some of the larger 34 mm dome HF units, where h may be 10 mm or so, this axial null may occur as low as 17 kHz and a gentle but progressive phase loss droop may be significant from 5 kHz upwards, assuming that no breakup occurs. Phase loss also applies to inverted domes, i.e. cones, but the breakup modes in these generally larger diaphragms usually begins at such low frequencies that the phase loss is unimportant.

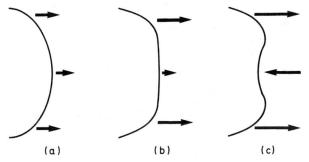

Figure 3.3   Dome behaviour leading to first breakup (a) piston operation at low frequencies; (b) at mid-frequencies, breakup beginning; (c) at resonance, centre out of phase with rim

Breakup modes

Even with dome units which are generally driven by a motor coil of the same diameter attached to the rim, the first breakup resonance usually occurs near or just before the first phase null, and the total output will then depend on the sum of the two effects.

The dome profile is chosen with due consideration for the strength, density and damping of the material used. Clearly a flat piston of given thickness is far less rigid and will have a much lower resonant frequency than a dome or cone structure of the same material. For this reason the shape may also be exploited to control resonances when they do occur; the contour may be selected so as to place the first resonance as high as possible, always remembering that any undamped resonances are undesirable. The degree of internal damping offered by the diaphragm is a further factor.

The first breakup resonance is an arbitrary name for the frequency at which the apex area of the diaphragm moves in anti-phase with the rim (Fig.3.3). The output at resonance depends on the damping and may, if suitably coincident with the phase null, provide some compensation for the latter towards the upper end of the frequency range.

3.2 VELOCITY OF SOUND IN A DIAPHRAGM

The velocity of sound in a structure is not so much dependent on its density and the elasticity of the material used, as on the actual structure or shape into which it is formed. Clearly when the velocity of sound in a diaphragm differs from that in air such that a phase difference can develop between the radiation from areas close to, and those remote from the motor drive, then a loss in output will occur.

At low frequencies where piston operation holds, the sound velocity

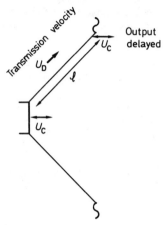

Figure 3.4   Velocity of sound in cones. (Assuming cone is shallow and hence depth negligible, the transit time t = U_D/l, *where* U_D = *velocity in diaphragm*

in a cone is high, i.e. three or four times that in air. With increasing frequency the velocity reduces, following an almost hyperbolic law. Breakup modes result in sharp irregular departures from this curve, but a cone with well controlled breakup modes may follow it quite slosely.

For example, a 200 mm frame size, pulp-paper cone possesses a sound velocity at 750 Hz, (approximately its first breakup mode) which is about equal to that in air. With a further increase in frequency, the velocity approaches the value for a flat sheet of the same diaphragm material of infinite size, in this case about 100 m/s or less than one third of the sound velocity in air.

Hence we have established another factor, namely a source of 'phase loss' caused by the time difference between radiation from the edges and centre of a diaphragm due to propagation velocity. Strictly speaking, this is another way of looking at the breakup or loss of rigidity phenomenon. Taking the example of the pulp cone mentioned above, a dip in response will occur when the delay generates a half-wavelength difference in the radiation between the centre and rim; the propagation time lag due to the cone height must also be considered (Fig.3.4).

It is interesting to speculate on the effect of this propagation delay. For pure piston operation the apex or centre radiation lags the rim output for a distant observer, this being equivalent to the dome phase loss discussed. The effect of this propagation delay is a retardation of the rim energy thus bringing it closer to the phase of the centre energy. By suitable control of geometry and other constants, it is possible to balance these two effects to some degree. Inspection shows that this same balance is also possible with a dome over a limited frequency range.

In practice both cone velocity and geometric phase loss effects must be considered of secondary importance by comparison with the dominant breakup modes. See Appendix 2.

3.3 COMPENSATION OF DOME CHARACTERISTICS

In most dome radiators the three effects described above work in unison. There is a propagation delay in the diaphragm which produces a phase lag between the apex and rim outputs, while 'phase loss' due to the height results in a phase lead, and finally the first breakup mode gives a more or less well damped resonance.

With suitable choice of motor design and careful choice of diaphragm thickness, material and contour, it is possible to obtain a usefully wide and uniform characteristic.

3.4 CONE BEHAVIOUR

With dome diaphragms the working frequency range rarely extends significantly beyond the first resonance mode described. However, the larger cone-type diaphragms are more susceptible to undesirable breakup or departure from true piston operation at relatively low frequencies, and of necessity they are often used well into their breakup range, even in high performance systems. The best known example is the extensive use of a type of thermoplastic coned, 200 mm frame, bass-mid range unit, covering the range 50 Hz to 3 kHz in compact enclosures of 30—50 litres volume. This is particularly prevalent among UK system designers. It would be no exaggeration to place the first breakup mode in this example as low as 700 Hz, and yet with careful design the colouration can remain low. The equalised axial response may hold to within ±1.5 dB limits right up to the 3 kHz crossover point.

A dome diaphragm is normally driven at the rim or perimeter and hence the path length is correspondingly short. In contrast, cones are driven from a relatively small apex area, the cone diameter generally 5 or 10 times larger. In this case the path length is appreciable and is responsible for the earlier breakup.

3.5 CONE PARAMETERS

There are a number of variables involved in the design of a cone (Fig.3.5):

(1)   material thickness and density, which may be non-uniform: some cones are intentionally thicker at the apex and thinner towards the edge

(2)   stiffness (or Young's modulus) of the material used

(3)   cone angle and profile: whether straight sided or flared

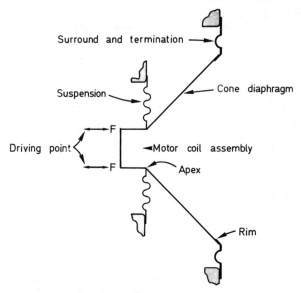

Figure 3.5   Cone diaphragm and suspension

(4)   absolute dimensions of the cone: its height, rim and apex diameter

(5)   rigidity and mass of the attached motor coil, and

(6)   suspension and mechanical properties of the surround.

An elementary model of cone behaviour may be established from vibration theory but this bears little relevance to real cones, as they are often highly variable and hence lack correspondence with any theory. This failure is partly due to the great complexity of the analysis involved but is mainly attributable to the anisotropy of the cone material. This is commonly an impregnated felted paper, whose mechanical properties can vary up to 100% in a random manner over the surface area. However, the use of vacuum formed plastics for cones and recent improvements in paper technology have resulted in rather closer correspondence with the theoretical predictions.

Transmission-line analogy

A cone possesses finite stiffness, distributed mass and some mechanical damping.   Assuming for the moment that the damping is high with negligible 'free' resonances, the area of the cone vibrating will tend to contract towards the driving point with increasing frequency. Thus the outer areas become increasingly decoupled from the centre due to the elasticity and mass of the material and in this case, the cone may be likened to a lossy transmission-line, or low-pass filter (Fig.3.6).

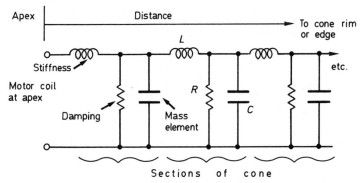

Figure 3.6   Transmission line analogue of loudspeaker cone (direction of reducing cutoff-frequency from left to right, i.e. lowpass filter action

This aspect of behaviour may be exploited by suitable cone design. One effect of this reducing cone area is to maintain an adequate dispersion to higher frequencies than would be expected from this size of driver, while the reducing mass results in augmented efficiency as the working cone mass approaches the mass of the motor coil.

Termination

Sound energy applied to the cone apex by a motor coil propagates towards the rim. It is undiminished at low frequencies but will be attenuated at higher frequencies due to the low-pass transmission filter effect described. If poorly terminated, as in the extreme case when the edge is directly clamped to the frame, (a short circuit) or alternatively left free, (an open circuit) the incident energy will be strongly reflected back towards the apex. This will not only interfere with the prime outward travelling energy, thus setting up standing waves, but it may also excite more complex vibrational modes in the cone.

For this reason, the surround must present a well matched resistive, or lossy mechanical termination to the cone rim. It should efficiently absorb the incident energy at higher frequencies while not introducing excessive mechanical loss at low frequencies where the cone excursion may be considerable. The surround profile should be dimensioned so that it has no significant self-resonances (see Chapter 5).

The perfectly homogeneous cone

In theory, a homogenous or uniform cone should possess only one group of nodal resonances, these occurring in the axis of excitation (see Fig. 3.7a, b and c). This behaviour is illustrated by the aluminium-foil/

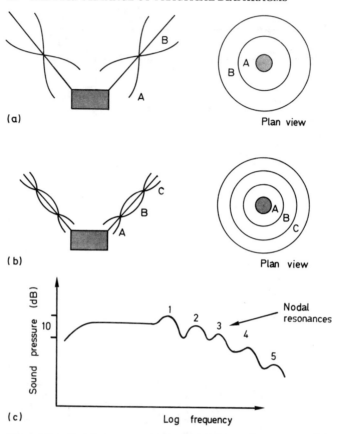

Figure 3.7   Nodal resonances (concentric); (a) 1st nodal resonance, (b) 2nd nodal resonance, (c) effect of nodal resonances on response

polystyrene-foam core 'sandwich' cones, which are extremely uniform over their surface area.

Normal cones

While the basic nodal or concentric resonances certainly occur in normal cones, they may be heavily disguised by other modes which can be excited as a result of diaphragm non-uniformity. The concentric modes are significant at high frequencies, and lower frequency irregularities may be produced by 'bell mode' or radial vibrations (Fig.3.8). Since their greatest amplitude is at the rim, both the rim contour and surround are critical factors in the control of these latter breakup effects.

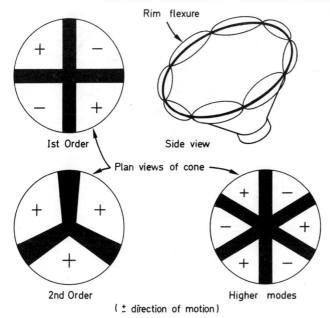

Figure 3.8   Radial or circumferential 'bell' modes

The 'bell modes' may be properly terminated, but the mechanical impedance match differs from that required to terminate the longitudinal or concentric mode energy.

With flared thermoplastic cones[3] employing a surround of plasticised p.v.c., it is possible to deal with both modes satisfactorily. The material's bulk properties in sheet form terminates the concentric modes and an extra flat section in the surround contour provides control of the radial modes (Fig.3.9).

Subharmonics

The mechanical non linearities in a vibrating cone can give rise to subharmonics of the fundamental excitation, that is at one half, one third frequency, etc., although only the first mode is generally of significance. Subharmonics usually only occur in thin straight sided cones. Cone angle and the other associated constants are all influential factors.

Cone material damping

The cone resonance modes may also be controlled by using a material

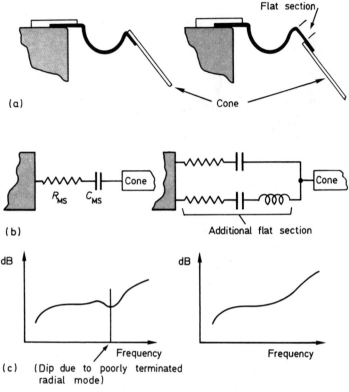

Figure 3.9   Effects of changes in the form of a half-roll surround. (a) Form: conventional and with flat section added, (b) equivalent circuit, (c) sound pressure response

which has a high internal damping. Although many cones are described as being made of paper, this material is more correctly specified as a dense felt, impregnated with a suitable stiffening agent. The loss factor may be varied at will, but it should be noted that the high frequency response extension will be strongly related to the amount of damping. With thermoplastic cones the polymer may be selected for its high damping coefficient, (e.g. Bextrene, a polystyrene/neoprene mixture) and may have an additional surface treatment coating such as poly-vinyl acetate (e.g. Plastiflex).

The very best examples of cone driver employ every favourable combination of construction and material to achieve their high performance.

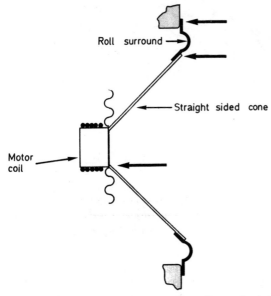

Roll surround

Straight sided cone

Motor coil

Figure 3.10 Straight sided cone profile. The mechanical impedance changes at the points arrowed, due to both material and rapid contour changes

3.6 CONE SHAPE

It has been demonstrated that cone shape is of great importance, and this fact cannot be emphasised too strongly. Even where a basic shape has been determined in advance, if the highest standards are demanded, as many as ten or more cone profiles may be experimented with before the optimum is finally obtained. Individual cone shapes will now be examined in greater detail.

Straight sided or true cones

The extreme case of a wide angle cone, (i.e. $180°$) is a flat disc. If light and thin, it will possess very little rigidity, and hence will enter breakup at quite low frequencies. This may be regarded as a special case which is seldom encountered. (See resistance controlled moving coil driver in Section 5.6).

As the angle is reduced the axial stiffness will increase, with a consequent rise in velocity of sound in the cone. The first resonance then occurs at a higher frequency and both circumferential and concentric modes appear (Fig.3.10).

With further angle reduction the increased axial rigidity continues to defer the first appearance of resonance and the concentric modes in-

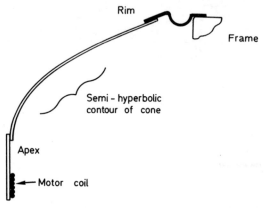

Figure 3.11   Example of cone surround profile of a high performance 305 mm driver (after Harwood)

crease in strength, these lifting the high frequency response, often with considerable irregularity. Somewhere in this range, with a given material, there may be an optimum angle where the smoothest extension of response is obtained without serious lower frequency resonances.

Curved profiles

One obvious defect of a straight sided cone, namely its strong circumferential mode resonance, may be effectively suppressed by the adoption of a flared or curved profile. This possesses greater rigidity with respect to these bending resonances.

A further defect concerns the discontinuities or corners presented by a straight sided cone at the two junctions; motor coil and apex, rim and surround. A flared cone may be shaped to provide a smooth contour from motor coil to rim surround, which considerably reduces the severity of the standing wave reflections at these boundaries. A flared cone will give less output over the upper resonant frequency range than will a straight sided cone, and hence will not be as 'loud', but its overall range exhibits greater uniformity and hence it is more suitable for high performance purposes.

However the flare must not be too shallow, otherwise the cone as a whole may prove insufficiently rigid to act as a piston under high-power, high excursion, conditions at low frequencies. Additionally an excessively open flare may allow the outer area to flex in anti-phase to the main output at mid frequencies.

Flares close to a hyperbolic law (Fig.3.11) have been successfully manufactured in many materials ranging from doped paper-felt to thermoplastics, and also in metals, notably aluminium and titanium.

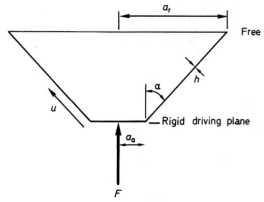

Figure 3.12   Cone analysis parameters
   (1) a_r, rim radius
   (2) a_a, apex radius
   (3) α, cone angle
   (4) h, material thickness
   (5) u, propagation velocity
   (6) E, Young's modulus
   (7) ρ, density
   (8) v, Poisson's ratio
   (9) δ, internal loss-factor

Analysis of a straight sided cone

The speaker research division of Philips in Holland has developed a method of analysing straight sided cones[4].

The typical form illustrated in Fig.3.12 is subject to bending (or circumferential) and longitudinal or (concentric/nodal) resonance modes. The arc of the bending wavelengths is typically much shorter than those equivalent frequencies in air, and hence has less effect on the output than the longitudinal resonance wavelengths whose dimensions are generally much greater than in air. The latter thus produce phase cancellation effects with consequent irregularities in the axial pressure response and the polar distribution.

In the analysis, the cone is described by four geometrical and four material parameters. The apex is rigidly driven by an axial sinusoidal force whose magnitude is independent of frequency. The radiation impedance is assumed to be negligible, (this is valid for most 'hi-fi' drivers with efficiencies of 0.5 to 2.0%), and the outer edge is assumed 'free'. Internal losses are also taken into account.

The breakup behaviour is represented by twelve simultaneous differential equations which were numerically solved over a wide frequency range. In the example quoted a paper-felt cone with an included angle of $100°$ and an outer diameter of 160 mm, was measured and its sound pressure and breakup patterns calculated.

Figures 3.13 and 3.14 illustrate the theoretical and measured curves. The discrepancy at low frequencies between the measured and calculated

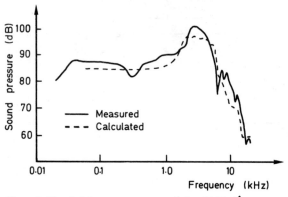

Figure 3.13   Axial pressure response (after Philips)[4]

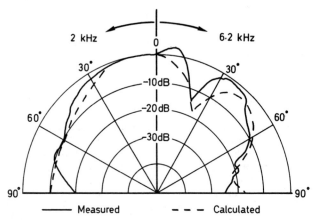

Figure 3.14   Directivity at two frequencies, 2 kHz and 6.2 kHz (after Philips)[4]

output is due to the additional contribution from the surround, a factor neglected in the theoretical approach. Likewise, the additional measured output around 10 kHz is attributed to the finite rigidity of the motor coil as opposed to the infinitely rigid structure assumed by the theory, and clearly the latter is quite realistic. The analysis also indicates that the transmission line analogue (Fig.3.6) is oversimplified.

3.7 MOTOR SYSTEMS

Up to now this chapter has mainly been concerned with pistons and diaphragms driven by hypothetical motors, that is convertors of electrical power into mechanical force. However, the elements of the moving coil motor were introduced in Section 2.3 dealing with the analysis of a

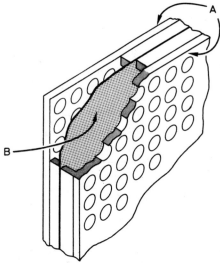

Figure 3.15   Section of an electrostatic transducer (after Jordan). A: Front and rear perforated electrodes (conductive). B: Very thin film diaphragm of high surface resistivity (10^{12} ohm/square)

direct radiator cone driver, and these will now be examined in greater detail.

In theory a diaphragm may be energised by a number of transducer principles, with the diaphragm characteristics (mass and area) being dimensioned to match these.

Film transducers

The large surface area transducer has always had a following. If uniformly driven over its surface area, such a low mass diaphragm will have a dominant resistive air loading which will tend to suppress any resonances. Theoretically such a transducer should also be efficient, due to the excellent radiation coupling. In practice however, engineering limitations reduce the efficiency to a level at or below that of the average moving coil driver. The best known and longest lived example is probably the Quad loudspeaker (Figs.3.15 and 3.16), which employs electrostatic drive to a light plastic film diaphragm.[5] This is a two-way, push—pull system with a high surface-resistivity diaphragm ensuring constant charge operation. The two elements of push—pull electrodes and constant charge impart linear operation up to fairly high frequencies and amplitudes, a performance not possible with the simple electrostatic driver employing a single fixed electrode.

Quad proposals for a new design outline a single acoustically transparent membrane excited by concentric ring electrodes fed from an equalised delay line. The constructed acoustic wave simulates a point source approximately 0.3 m behind the diaphragm[11].

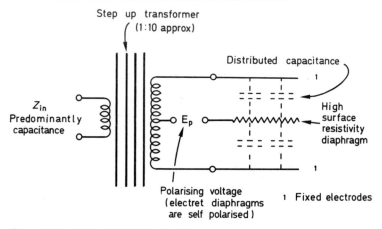

Figure 3.16   Electrostatic driver circuit

Other large area transducers have employed a variant of the moving coil whereby the 'turns' are laid out uniformly over the area of the film diaphragm, with the necessary static magnetic field supplied by an array of powerful magnets. Sufficient gaps must be provided to allow the sound energy produced to escape.

It would be wrong to suppose that the beneficial air mass/mass ratio will eliminate resonances entirely. In fact, a number of more or less well damped breakup modes are present which are akin to those occurring in a thin plate clamped at its edges. With some designs additional damping has proved necessary in the form of a local sympathetic vibrating membranes and/or surface diaphragm coatings. This is particularly true of the higher mass magnetic diaphragms.

To date, no film loudspeaker has proved to be particularly cost effective or electrically efficient. Due to a rigid constraint of field strength versus allowable diaphragm displacement, which restricts the resulting sensitivity, there are definite limits as to the maximum sound level that can be attained. For the magnetic types, the sheer cost of the high-energy magnets is prohibitive, and on the electrostatic side, the combination of voltage breakdown and the reactive input impedance of the capacitive element together act to restrict the maximum acoustic power output.* Where high levels are required, these large systems are also considerably more directional than well designed direct radiators, although with care the dispersion may still be adequate over the important part of the range.

In recent years, electret elements have been developed for use in headphone sets and microphones, where the polarising potential is present in the form of a permanent charge akin to magnetisation. Large drivers for loudspeaker applications may well be developed along these lines.

* Walker's important new paper[11] describes a far reaching combination of design factors which largely solves the input impedance and directivity problems.

TABLE 3.1. SOME EXAMPLES OF FILM-TYPE TRANSDUCERS

Electrostatic
(1)   Dayton Wright Electrostatic — An array of convex elements with a sulphur
      hexafluoride filling to increase dielectric strength and hence allow higher
      voltage operation. A horn super tweeter is often used with this system.

(2)   Quad Electrostatic — Classic two way system of adequate power capacity.

(3)   KLH 9 — Electrostatic multi-way system in a tall, vertical panel format,
      with strip elements for the higher frequencies.

(4)   Accustat — large angled panel full-range system with direct-coupled valve
      amplifier eliminating transformer/polariser

Magnetic
(1)   Magneplanar — A large panel transducer with a mylar film disphragm using
      copper wire bonded over its surface area.

(2)   Strathearn — A magnetic drive film transducer with a transformer coupled
      single foil turn, and strip magnets (mid and treble range only)

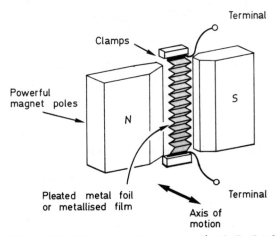

Figure 3.17   Ribbon transducer element (typically 5 × 25 mm). May be horn-loaded to improve air coupling

The ribbon

The so called 'ribbon' is a variant of the film transducer and comprises
a thin corrugated conducting foil placed between the poles of a power-
full magnet, thus constituting a single turn very low impedance coil
(Fig.3.17). As with the normal solenoid type motor coil, the motion is at
right angles to both the coil and magnetic axes, the ribbon equating to

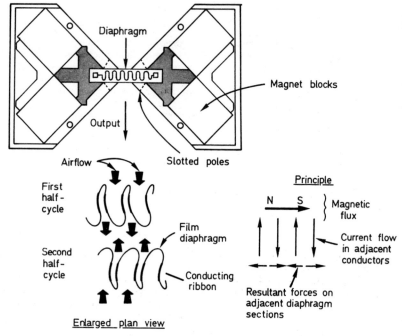

Figure 3.18   Heil 'Air Motion Transformer' (after ESS)

a diaphragm element clamped at each end. It is difficult to produce large ribbons, due to problems of generating a sufficiently high field strength over a wide magnet gap, and hence the transducer is usually horn coupled to achieve reasonable air matching and efficiency. A transformer is also required to match the amplifier to the very low impedance of the conducting element.

Air-motion transformer

The so called 'air-motion transformer' is a device which was developed in the States by Oskar Heil, and resembles a ribbon driver in construction (Fig.3.18). The vital element in this case is a pleated plastic film diaphragm with a metalised conductor pattern of normal 6 Ω or so resistance. The forward/aft motion of a 'ribbon' is not exploited and instead, the element is encouraged to expand and contract along its length like a bellows, this action pumping air in and out of the folds. This is claimed to result in a 5:1 magnification of the air load presented to the diaphragm, resulting in good damping and reasonable efficiency.

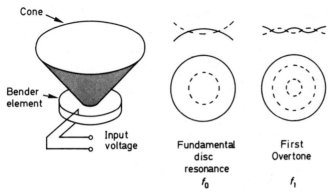

Figure 3.19   Piezo-electric horn driver element, working range between f_0 *and* f_1
(cone may be coupled to short slotted horn — not shown). (Courtesy Motorola)[6]

Certainly the performance of the commercial examples available would
tend to bear out this claim.

At present a 400 Hz to 20 kHz range is possible, and research is continuing on a larger mechanical version of the 'air pump' for bass frequencies, using a solenoid type motor element.   High internal loss
materials (such as polyethylene or teflon (p.t.f.e.)) are used for the film
in the present HF models as these inhibit self resonances.

Piezo-electric and high-polymer transducers

Certain materials have the property of a dimensional changes when an
electric potential is applied across them, this being a reversible mechanism.   Both crystalline substances such as Rochelle salt, and the so
called ceramics such as barium titanate, demonstrate this piezo-electric
effect. Some plastics known as high-polymers have also been developed
that possess this property: incidentally, these are polarised internally
like electrets. The piezo-electric effect in these polyvinylidene—fluoride
'high polymers' can be up to ten times that of quartz.

The high mechanical impedance of the mineral substances normally
restricts their use to high frequencies: one design employs a ceramic
element, this being a horn loaded HF unit (Fig.3.19) developed by
Motorola[6]. It uses a circular 'bender' 22.6 mm in diameter and 0.5 mm
thick, and a small cone is joined to the centre of the element, this
acoustically coupling the latter to a moulded semi-sectoral horn.   The
axial response covered is 4 kHz to 20 kHz, within ±3.0 dB limits.

Although high-polymer 'benders' may also be produced, another use
for this material has been suggested. If a thin film (30 μ) of high-
polymer plastic is formed into a cylinder (Fig.3.20) the dimensiona
changes under applied electric field variation will cause the cylinder's

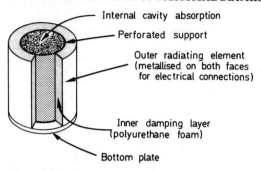

Figure 3.20   Cylindrical high-polymer Piezo HF unit (Courtesy Pioneer)[7]

radius to pulsate. Such a structure approximates almost perfectly to a theoretical cylindrical source[7].

With additional damping and support elements, cylindrical section mid and treble range drivers have been constructed with a voltage sensitivity similar to that of typical moving coil drivers. The input impedance is of course high and predominantly capacitive.

Magnetic circuits and motor coils

The most widely used motor system is the cylindrical coil immersed in a strong radial magnetic field, usually generated by a permanent magnet.

The force on the coil is given by $F = Bll$, where B = the flux density, l the length of wire immersed in the magnetic flux and I the current (Fig.3.21). The coil/cone velocity is represented by $U = F/Z_M$ where Z_M is the total mechanical impedance reflected on the coil. (See Section 2.3).

The transducer action is reversible and hence cone motion gives rise to a corresponding current in the coil. This is the so called 'back e.m.f.' and is reflected in the motional impedance of the coil.

Although Z_M is a mechanical impedance it may be transformed into an electrical equivalent, Z_{EM}, via the motor relation to give

$$Z_{EM} = \frac{B^2 l^2}{Z_M}$$

The total input impedance of a moving coil driver also includes the coil resistance and associated inductance (Fig.3.22), hence

$$Z_{in} = j\omega L_c + R_c + \frac{B^2 l^2}{Z_M}$$

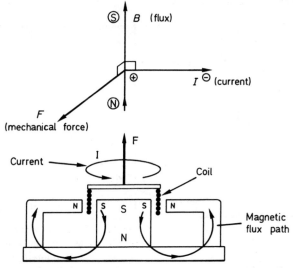

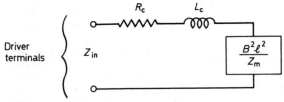

Figure 3.21   (a) Electromagnetic motor principle. (b) Moving-coil motor element

Figure 3.22   Moving coil driver equivalent circuit (electrical side), where Z_{in} is the total impedance and Z_M is the total mechanical impedance, i.e. moving system and air load

Figure 3.23 shows variations in input impedance of a typical moving coil driver mounted in free air. The impedance curve may be readily measured via a constant current source and gives much useful information about a driver.

3.8 MOVING-COIL MOTOR LINEARITY

Ignoring the contribution of the suspension or surround, the magnetic motor will itself possess non-linearities due to the magnetic gap flux deviating from a theoretically uniform radial field. This is attributable to fringing effects at the edges of the poles, which result in the magnetic field extending beyond the gap. For maximum flux utilisation most short-throw coils are overwound by a factor of some 15% in length, in order to make full use of the available flux.

Low frequency resonance

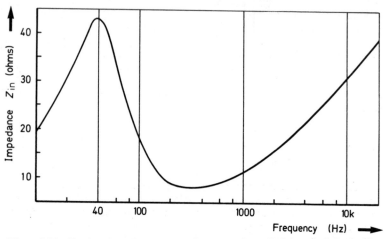

Figure 3.23   Typical impedance curve for a moving-coil driver (infinite baffle mounted) (see also Fig.6.10)

The output is fundamentally dependent on B times l, the product of the flux density and the wire length immersed. If a coil undergoes considerable excursion, as is required to reproduce low frequencies at a reasonable power level, it will move from one region of flux density to another while the coil portion in the useable flux may also change, this in combination producing non-linear drive and consequent distortion. Such a driver under considerable excursion at low frequencies will also produce intermodulation with the mid-range, the latter output showing an amplitude variation due to the modulated Bl factor. Another secondary effect concerns the coil inductance which may be a significant part of the driver's input impedance at mid and high frequencies. This inductance may be coil position dependent, in which case it will vary in sympathy with the excursion, thus adding a further modulation factor.

There are two obvious methods available to improve linearity. One consists of lengthening the coil to twice or possibly three times the magnet gap length, while the other utilises a short coil fully immersed in a longer gap. Both solutions allow a given length to occupy a constant flux within the designed excursion limits, but they are costly in terms of efficiency. In the case of the long coil, a large proportion of the input power is wasted in coil resistance, as only a percentage of the turns are active. For the short coil only a small proportion of the available flux is used one time, thus necessitating an overlarge magnet system.

On economic grounds, the long coil presents the most attractive solution and is widely used for long throw, low efficiency, low frequency units.   The increased coil area results in an improved thermal power handling but gives an increase in both coil mass and inductance, these tending to curtail the output in the mid and upper range.

Where acoustic demands are reasonable, that is a high efficiency is not required, the high performance bass-mid range units have generally made use of the short coil option.   Some designers have suggested compensation methods involving non-linear coil winding or specially shaped pole faces, but unfortunately both are costly and involve a further loss of efficiency.

Instability

Examination of the variation of average flux-linked turns, (or Bl factor) for a coil under large excursion, shows that Bl reduces at the amplitude peaks where the coil begins to leave the gap.   In the region above the fundamental resonance where the coil driver is under mass control, the motional impedance is still considerable and the back e.m.f. at the driver terminals is both correspondingly high and proportional to $(Bl)^2$.   As the coil moves away from the central rest position, the back e.m.f. is reduced due to the lowered Bl factor, and hence more power is drawn from the amplifier, (assuming a normal constant voltage source).   This drives the coil proportionately further, the process accelerating until the coil is constantly displaced away from the zero position, this resulting in extreme distortion.[8]   The moving coil system is thus fundamentally unstable in this respect. High compliance systems with a large cone mass are particularly susceptible and I have known some poor designs thermally rated at 100 W to 'lock out' with as little as 6 W input at 100 Hz.

Clearly long coil or long gap design helps to reduce the Bl variation and minimises the effect.   Good suspension design can ensure that the system mechanically 'soft limits' before the jump-out excursion is attained.   This intentional suspension non-linearity is to be preferred to the almost 100% half-wave distortion which occurs during jump-out. Investigation has shown that with reflex loading the effects are more severe than with sealed box.   This is partially due to the lack of box volume stiffness helping to restore the diaphragm/coil to the linear range, but more importantly to the high sensitivity of a reflex system to variations in damping or Bl product.

Towards jump-out the reduced Bl allows the system to 'ring' or overshoot excessively at the box resonance.   By suitable design[10] two low resistance conductive rings may be added, adjacent to each end of the motor coil.   These provide substantial eddy loss damping at the excursion extremes providing a considerable linearisation at high amplitudes and thus an effective correction for both 'instability' and Bl linearity in general.

Distortion compensation

The suspension non-linearity may be balanced against the magnetic instability since the former is negative, (wavelength compression with increasing excursion) and the latter positive, (wavelength expansion with increasing excursion). Obviously with a given system this may be taken to a certain power level, beyond which the cancellation fails, producing gross distortion.[9]

By using a slightly oversized coil with a suitable choice of suspension and surround, the power handling for a given distortion level may be increased by 3 to 5 dB above that possible with a conventional unmatched suspension. Incidentally, the non-linearity of the air stiffness may also have to be taken into account.

Power improvement due to fringing

The presence of magnetic fringing has been mentioned in the context of gap flux non-uniformity. Harwood has pointed out that in terms of power capacity it potentially allows a better match between the suspension and Bl non linearities. In the case of a specific driver, a 6 dB improvement in low frequency handling was produced over that expected, due to this compensation.

Combined suspension and motor design

The benefits of integrating the design of the motor system and suspension are now apparent. In some cases, a similar coil/gap length may be chosen for optimum efficiency. The suspension stiffness and total non-linearity may be used to both extend the power output by nearly 10 dB and prevent jump-out. The choice of a sensible coil length also results in sensible values of inductance and mass, thus improving the upper range output and reducing the position dependency of the coil inductance.

A driver designed along these lines is likely to exhibit a rather higher fundamental resonance than the typical long throw low frequency unit; for example, 35 Hz as against 20 Hz, and consequently reflex loading is more usual with these optimised medium resonance drivers.

Coil inductance and its suppression

Several methods have been suggested for suppressing coil inductance which are all essentially the same in principle. These involve placing a shorted turn in the magnetic coil system, such as a conducting motor coil former or a second coil or the use of copper shielded or plated magnetic poles. The circulating current induced in the copper 'turn' will reduce the motor coil inductance and will also shunt higher frequency eddy currents from the magnetic poles, a factor which can produce residual harmonic distortion in some drivers. If a shielding method is not employed, the latter effect may be overcome by laminating the poles, as is done in wide-band audio-transformer cores.

The 'shorted turn' will also have an effect on the back e.m.f. in the motor coil at low frequencies, particularly at the driver's main resonance, as it will reduce the magnitude of resonance slightly, due to eddy current

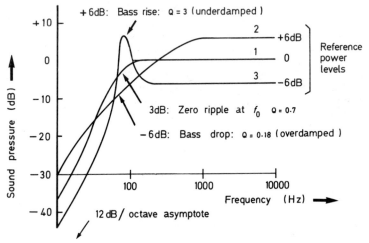

Figure 3.24   Variation of sealed-box system response for three values of flux density; (1) maximally flat Butterworth flux level, (2) flux density doubled (initial roll-off at 6 dB/octave) and (3) flux density halved (+12 dB 'bass boom')

loss.   However, the effective coupling factor at low frequencies is small, and in consequence it can be ignored.

One disadvantage of such a copper turn or sleeve arrangement is the reduction in magnet efficiency, since to be effective the copper needs to occupy 20–30% of the gap thickness, with a consequent reduction in flux density.

The effective improvement in rise time or transient high frequency response due to coil inductance cancellation has been incorrectly described as a major advantage for bass units, where the inductance of a large, long throw coil may be considerable.   However this is a false assumption, as the system transient performance and rise time is largely determined by the highest frequency unit in the system, that is the HF driver, and has no connection with the bass unit.   The LF transient response is a function of the low frequency resonance and its damping, which are unaffected by considerations of coil inductance.

3.9 INFLUENCE OF MAGNETIC FIELD STRENGTH ON LOUD-SPEAKER PRESSURE RESPONSE

With loudspeaker diaphragm assemblies falling within a prescribed range of mass for good colouration and response, the other major design responsible for efficiency is the magnetic field strength of flux density, B.

Figure 3.24 shows the influence of B on a typical driver; (LF design will be considered in detail in Chapter 4).   Curve 1 illustrates an optimum magnet strength, 3 shows the effect halving the field and 2 that for doubling the field.   The uniform reference response band shows

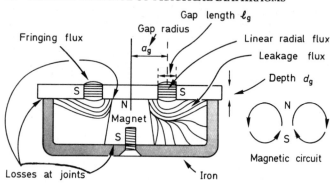

Figure 3.25   Typical Alnico 'pot' magnet structure

expected changes of ±6 dB. i.e. the output here is proportional to the square of the flux change.

At low frequencies near resonance the results are perhaps the reverse of what might be expected. The larger magnet has actually halved the LF power at resonance through over-damping, and since the mid-band has risen 6 dB, the effective bass loss totals 12 dB. By contrast the smaller magnet has reduced the damping to below optimum, giving a 6 dB rise in bass, this exacerbated by the accompanying 6 dB fall in mid-band level, and resulting in an effective bass boost of 12 dB.

This example demonstrates that magnet strength may not be indiscriminately increased or reduced. There will be an optimum Bl value for any design of enclosure, driver and loading (see Chapter 4).

3.10 MAGNET SYSTEMS

The high sensitivity of a system's output to flux strength variations means that most magnet designs are operated with the poles saturated, in order to attain a more constant field in production. This necessarily implies a wastage of available flux. Further loss occurs in the leakage paths and at the physical interfaces between the magnetic components.

It is not uncommon for poorly designed commercial magnet systems to utilise as little as 10% of the total flux in producing acoustic power.

The gap geometry (see Fig.3.25) must be dimensioned so that the motor coil assembly, with the required wire length, may be accommodated with sufficient clearance for normal scrape-free movement. It must also include provision for manufacturing tolerances and aging drift in the cone suspensions. Clearly a short-throw coil will require less gap margin than a long-throw version and hence will allow greater utilisation of gap flux.

The ratio of gap to pole dimensions will determine the degree of magnetic leakage and hence how much wasted flux is left outisde the working gap. This factor may vary between 2 and 10 for various pole and magnet geometries. The relevant parameters for a magnetic material are B and H, respectively flux density and coercive force. The optimum working point is usually where the $B \times H$ product is at a maximum, in other words, at the knee of the curve.

Magnet design

The following relations govern the design and specification of the energising magnet and the magnetic circuit required.

The fundamental energy factor in a moving coil loudspeaker is the Bl product, where l is the length of coil wire immersed in a magnet flux density B. The geometry of the gap, i.e. coil or centre pole radius a_g, gap thickness or depth d_g, and the gap width l_g together with the required flux density B_g will determine the other parameters.

For the gap

$$H_g . k_B = H_m$$

and

$$H_g = B_g A_g$$

where H_g = total gap flux; k_B = a loss factor; H_m = total magnet flux; B_g = gap flux density, and A_g = gap area.

Also

$$H_m = B_m A_m$$

where B_m = magnet flux density, and A_m = magnet area.

Hence the magnet surface area

$$A_m = \frac{k_B B_g A_g}{B_m}$$

Substituting the gap dimensions for A_g

$$A_m = \frac{k_B B_g d_g . 2a_g}{B_m}$$

The magnetic potential across the gap equals that across the joints, pole paths and magnet, this is analogous to a static electric circuit where the generator potential equals the sum of the potentials across each series circuit element. The potential across each magnetic element depends on their reluctance, which is a function of the material and

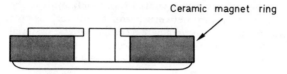

Figure 3.26   Typical ceramic magnet structure illustrating height/CSA ratio

geometry. A loss factor k_H of between 1.1 and 1.3 is associated with the potential circuit.

Thus

$$H_m L_m = H_g L_g k_H$$

and hence magnet length

$$L_m = \frac{H_g L_g k_H}{H_m}$$

If the flux density of the magnet is fixed, then the magnet dimensions may be found using the above equation.

An alnico or alcomax magnet will have a typical B value of 1.0 T and H values of 0.5, giving similar proportions to those illustrated (Fig.3.25). In contrast a ceramic magnet will have B close to 0.25 T and H at 0.12, which as can be seen from the above equation, will produce a magnet with low profile proportions (Fig.3.26).

The magnetic circuit efficiency is defined as $100/k_H$ and is the percentage of total flux used in the available gap flux. Operation of magnets at the knee or BH maximum implies they are virtually saturated, as is the case in practice, thus improving consistency. Loudspeaker drivers are usually assembled in the demagnetised condition to reduce risk of gap contamination. Magnet 'charging' is carried out at a final stage and the magnet design must take this requirement into account.

REFERENCES

1.   Kates, J. M., 'Radiation from a dome', *J. Audio Engng Soc.* 24, No. 9, 735–7 (1976)
2.   Yuasa, Y. and Greenberg, S., 'The beryllium dome diaphragm', *Proc. Audio Engng Soc. 52nd Convention,* October–November (1975)
3.   Harwood, H. D., 'New BBC monitoring loudspeaker', *Wireless World,* March, April and May (1968)
4.   Frankort, F. J. M., *Vibration And Sound Radiation Of Loudspeaker Cones,* (Philips Publications)
5.   Walker, P. J., 'Wide-range electrostatic loudspeakers', *Wireless World,* May, June and August (1955)

6.   Bost, J. R., 'A new type of tweeter horn employing a piezo-electric driver', *J. Audio Engng Soc.* 23, No.10, 796–801 (1975)
7.   Tamura, M., 'Electroacoustic transducer with piezo-electric high polymer films', *J. Audio Engng Soc.* 23, No.1, 21–6 (1975)
8.   Barlow, D. A., 'Instability in moving coil drivers', *Proc. Audio Engng Soc. 50th Convention,* London, March (1975)
9.   Harwood, H. D., 'Loudspeaker distortion associated with low frequency signals', *J. Audio Engng Soc.* 20, No.9, 718–28 (1972)
10.   SEAS Fabrikker AS, 'Dynamic Damping', Data Sheet (1978)
11.   Walker, P. J., 'New developments in electrostatic loudspeakers', *Audio Engng Soc. 63rd Convention Preprint* 1472 (D-10) (1979)

BIBLIOGRAPHY

Frankort, F. J. M., 'Vibration patterns and radiation behaviour of loudspeaker cones', *J. Audio Engng Soc.,* 26, No.11 (1978)
Fryer, P. A., 'The holographic investigation of speaker vibrations', *Proc. Audio Engng Soc. 50th Convention,* London, March (1975)
Gayford, M. L., *Acoustical Techniques And Transducers,* Macdonald and Evans, London (1961)
Hladky, J., 'Holography of loudspeaker diaphragms', *J. Audio Engng Soc.* 22, No.4, 247–250 (1974)
Jordan, E. J., *Loudspeakers,* Focal Press, London (1963)
Kates, J. M., 'Analysis of decoupled cone loudspeakers', *J. Audio Engng Soc.,* 25, No.1/2 (1977)
Kelly, S., 'Loudspeaker enclosure survey', *Wireless World,* 552–58, November (1972)
King, J., 'Loudspeaker voice coils', *J. Audio Engng Soc.* 18, No.1, 34–43 (1970)
Lian, R., 'Non-linear time delay distortion', *Proc. Audio Engng Soc. 47th Convention,* Copenhagen (1974)
Merhaut, J., 'A horn loaded electrostatic loudspeaker', *J. Audio Engng Soc.* 19 No.10, 804–6 (1971)
Millward, G. P., 'The isodynamic principle', *Proc. Audio Engng Soc. 50th Convention,* London, March (1975)
Sakamoto, N. et al., 'Frequency response considerations for an electrostatic horn tweeter using electret elements', *J. Audio Engng Soc.* 24, No.5, 268–373 (1976)
Whelan, R. C., 'A novel planiform loudspeaker system', *Proc. Audio Engng Soc. 50th Convention,* London, March (1975)

4

Acoustic loading and low frequency system analysis

It is relatively easy to measure the low frequency parameters of a drive unit. These relate to the most consistent and well defined area of operation where the diaphragm may be considered a true piston with hemispherical radiation properties.

Armed with the characteristics of the driver — moving mass, suspension compliance and the like — an equivalent circuit may be readily constructed for the driver and its enclosure, whether sealed or ported, (reflexed). The analysis brings out useful ways of looking at the system as a whole and the theory can be remarkably successful in predicting the low frequency performance of real loudspeakers provided that the practical details of manufacture, assembly and measurement are reasonably well controlled.

4.1 GENERAL CONSIDERATIONS

The initial theory of LF loading has been covered in Chapter 2, where the piston was mounted in three ways; in free space (finite baffle); on an infinite baffle and on the end face of an infinite cylinder. In this chapter only the lowest octaves will be considered and the directional characteristics at higher frequencies, noted in Section 2.1 will thus not apply. The impractical form of 'finite baffle' loading will have likewise been omitted, since the effective reproduction of low frequencies requires the use of an inordinantly large structure; (the large film diaphragms are a special case, see Chapter 3, Walker[5]). However it is worth noting that with an open baffle the rate of rolloff is 1st order, at 6 dB/octave; the most gentle slope of the LF loading methods.

The theory presented in this chapter generally assumes the speaker enclosure to be mounted in a large wall, with the system driving a large room volume whose dimensions are considerable compared with the lowest wavelengths under discussion. In accordance with the LF radiation pattern examined in Chapter 2, coverage is hemispherical, i.e. into a half-space, (2π steradians). However when the finite size of a typical listening room is taken into account, the situation is more complex. The effective radiation space will vary with frequency, this influencing the axial pressure response.

The term 'infinite baffle (IB) mounting' may be a source of confusion, as the surface of such a baffle is metaphorically brought round to the rear of the driver to form a closed or sealed box. The only practical approximation to a true infinite baffle consists of fitting a driver into a dividing wall between two rooms, a technique rarely employed for obvious reasons. In fact, the IB enclosure as we know it is more correctly termed a 'closed box'. Infinite baffle radiation theory does not hold true for a box system unless its front panel is flush mounted in a large wall. In practice this condition may be achieved only with small bookcase enclosures as the larger models are likely to be used in floor or stand mounted positions, located at some distance from an adjacent wall. Free standing location is employed for many high quality loudspeaker systems today and hence the relationship between 'IB' theory and the sound radiation from an enclosure in a room must also be taken into consideration. (Reflex systems may be considered as a sub-division of closed boxes.)

Room interaction

Take the case of a medium sized system designed to produce a uniform axial pressure response under anechoic conditions; (true free-field and not conventional small anechoic chamber measurement). If it is placed against a wall at frequencies where the enclosure is substantially omnidirectional, (below 200 Hz or so), the radiation in the forward plane will be doubled due to the addition of the reflected rear directed energy. Hence a +3 dB stepup in the sound pressure will occur below 200 Hz. If we were to add a floor to this hypothetical wall and place the enclosure at the boundary, then the effective radiation space is halved again, resulting in a further 3 dB lift at low frequencies. If a second wall were to be added, forming a corner, once again the axial pressure level will increase by 3 dB. Inspection of the radiation paths to the listening position shows that each adjacent wall is acting as an acoustic mirror, redirecting off-axis sound back into the forward plane. While this situation may be desirable on grounds of efficiency, the reflected images may cause interference with the direct path radiation and disturb the stereo effect. Furthermore, the greater the number of wall surfaces acoustically coupled to the reproducer, the stronger will be the excitation of the eigentones or room standing wave modes, a corner being the worst position in this respect[1].

Optimum system design for low subjective colouration

So far the most satisfactory subjective results have been obtained in the smaller listening rooms through minimising the coupling to the walls or floor. This is achieved by employing an open stand about 0.4 m high on which the enclosure is placed, the latter spaced clear of adjacent walls by more than 0.6 m. Unavoidably there will be some irregularity in the response at the listener position due to remaining room reflections but subjectively these do not appear to be too serious. By removing the enclosure from immediate contact with the floor, the frequency band at which severe local reflection begins is sufficiently low to minimise the colouration in the more important mid-band (300 Hz and upwards).

LF limitation due to room size

Below 200 Hz the enclosure will be less than a wavelength away from the floor and thus may be assumed in contact with it. At some lower frequency it will be joined by the nearest wall, and so on until the room dimensions themselves have been taken into account. This state of affairs partly explains why uniform low frequency reproduction in modest listening rooms is almost impossible to achieve. This does not mean to say that an extended low frequency response should not be aimed for, but does explain why larger rooms have a less coloured bass sound.

Integrated room/speaker design

One solution suggested by Allinson involves the deliberate exploitation of the low frequency radiation properties of the loudspeaker and listening room. He has shown that there exists an optimum driving point for the most uniform low frequency response, and that a system may be tailored both physically and electrically to make best use of this position. His paper illustrates a worthwhile improvement at low frequencies but gives indications that the mid-range quality may be affected[2]. This is precisely why the free space stand method described above has been widely adopted for high quality monitoring speaker installations.

It has recently been shown[28,29] that it is possible to simultaneously cope with the need for close coupling at low frequencies and offer dispersed semi-free field radiation at higher frequencies. The latter requirement is essential for the formation of precise unambiguous stereo images and also to minimise the type of colouration which makes small source sounds such as the human voice sound unnatural.

The technique consists in first choosing an appropriate crossover frequency between the low and mid frequency units — typically between 200 and 350 Hz. Secondly the enclosure/system is so designed that the MF unit is well clear of the floor and rear wall boundary, thus ensuring that the interference dips which are reflected on that driver's output actually appear below its crossover frequency. These occur at between 120 and 160 for a driver mounted between 0.4 and 0.6 m from the nearest boundary. Finally the LF unit is located in close

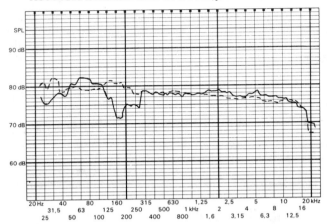

Figure 4.1   Comparison of two curves taken by multiple microphone position averaging in a domestic listening room. Both curves are for speaker systems with similar drivers. The dashed response applies to a cabinet with a close coupled LF driver and crossover separated mid range. The solid response is that of a conventional system with front mounted drivers in the same room location, i.e. 1.6 m from the side walls, rear of cabinet close to rear wall, and mid units at near ear level. The improvement in low frequency uniformity shown is typical for a number of microphone and speaker positions (after Acoustic Research)

proximity to the local boundaries, for example, on the side of the lowest available section of the floor mounted enclosure. The small spacing ensures that the boundary interference effects are located between 500 and 700 Hz outside of the L.F. driver's passband. By this means the problem of first order boundary interference is neatly sidestepped and no longer appears as an irregularity in the system's acoustic output in a conventional listening room (Fig.4.1).

At low frequencies a floor mounted enclosure, fairly closely positioned to the rear wall will have an acoustic load corresponding to π steradians rather than the 2π assumed in the theory for low frequency analysis. Some loss is to be expected due to wall and floor flexure and typically an overall gain of 2 dB is possible below 100 Hz. This adds further evidence to support the suggestion that the system Q factor should be on the low side, 0.5 rather than 0.7, to offset increasing room gain.

Relationship of anechoic to room response at low frequencies

It is understood that a close relationship exists between the measured low frequency response characteristic of the speaker in a small conventional anechoic chamber (i.e. in the near field), and the system's actual use in a similarly dimensioned listening room. This is implicit in the assumption that an anechoically derived uniform axial pressure response is a worthwhile goal for a high quality stand mounted system.

Optimum Q_{TC}

An interesting phenomenon has been noticed by the author concerning those stand mounted systems which possess an optimally damped LF characteristic (Q_{TC} of approximately 0.8 for a sealed box system) together with an equalised uniform axial free field pressure response. In conventional rooms, the bass response appears to be subjectively somewhat underdamped, this suggesting (and confirmed by experiment) that a degree of deliberate overdamping may be desirable. A sealed box Q_{TC} of 0.5 to 0.6 is indicated, this confirmed over a series of listening tests.

2π free-field standard acoustic load

Returning to the question of LF loading, the balance between our well defined range below 200 Hz and that above may be resolved by suitable enclosure positioning, and/or electrical equalisation. From now on, only the lowest three octaves will be discussed — 25 Hz to 200 Hz — and the radiation space taken as 2π steradians or a hemisphere, generally accepted as reasonably valid for wall mounted and free standing enclosures near domestic room boundaries.

4.2 LF SYSTEM ANALYSIS

Modern thinking is best illustrated by the many fine papers on the subject, the majority of which have appeared in the Journal of the Audio-Engineering Society (AES) or else been read at their conventions. The classic work on reflex systems (vented boxes) is that by Thiele[3] which was first presented as early as 1961. This represented both an effective summary of work to date as well as providing new viewpoints. A decade or so later Small[4-9] produced a series of papers on loudspeaker analysis which were republished in the Journal of the Audio Engineering Society the first appearing early in 1972. Those readers seeking a detailed treatment of the subject are strongly advised to acquire a set of these articles, as a single chapter in a book cannot do justice to all the available material.

Fundamental performance limitation

The performance limit of any simple box system[10] (excluding horns and the like) may be described by the following equation for efficiency, where η_0 is the efficiency in the level reference region.

$$\eta_0 = k_n f_3^3 V_B \tag{4.1}$$

where k_n is an efficiency constant, f_3 is the -3 dB low frequency rolloff point, and V_B is the box internal volume. The system is assumed to be driving a standard 2π sound field.

Of fundamental importance, this equation shows that for a given type of system and driver, any alteration of volume or cutoff frequency will also affect the efficiency. For example given a bass response to 70 Hz at -3 dB in a sealed box system, the efficiency may be doubled only by doubling the enclosure volume. Alternatively, it for the same starting efficiency the response were to be extended by an octave for example to 35 Hz, then the volume would have to be multiplied by a factor of eight.

This explains why compact, wide band systems are so inefficient and also suggests that the pursuit of an extended low frequency response for its own sake is likely to prove extremely costly and hence represents unbalanced engineering. Since little broadcast or disc programme contains significant energy below 35 Hz, the desire for substantial LF extension is rather pointless.

Magnitude of k_n

k_n is an efficiency factor which depends on the following; the class of system, i.e. sealed or ported; the system losses; the required response shape or alignment, and the driver–enclosure compliance ratio.

Maximum values may be estimated, with practical limits for a well designed system calculated to be $k_n = 2 \times 10^{-6}$ for a reflex loaded system and 1×10^{-6} for a sealed box (MKS units)[10].

Referring to the example on reference efficiency in Section 2.4, the driver examined is suitable for sealed box loading in a 30 litre enclosure, and will possess a -3 dB frequency at 50 Hz. Using the limitation Equation 4.1 above gives

$$\eta_0 = 50^3 \times 30 \times 10^{-3} \times 10^{-6} = 0.37\%,$$

which compares well with the reference efficiency calculated using the driver constants. It is however important to note that the driver size does not appear in the equation. Theoretically, by ignoring practical factors such as diaphragm excursion limits, any driver size could be used in any practicable enclosure. With respect to low frequency reproduction, there are no intrinsic magic properties possessed by large cones as opposed to small. Simply, larger drivers are ultimately capable of radiating greater acoustic power for a given distortion level.

High-pass filter analogy

A driver-box assembly may be represented as a high-pass filter. The sealed box equates to a 2nd order network with a 12 dB/octave rolloff below the cutoff frequency, while the reflex system is a 4th order network, with a 24 dB/octave rolloff. A 3rd order response, 18 dB/octave may be obtained by the addition of a series high-pass element in the electrical circuit of a closed box system. An approximation to a third order rolloff over a limited range (about 1.5 octaves) may be obtained by resistively or otherwise over-damping a fourth order reflex system. (Multi-bore or fabric blocked ports can provide the box resonance damping.) A double cavity enclosure system fed electrically via a first order bandpass filter[27] can offer an overall third order 18 dB/octave bandpass response over three octaves, this relevant to sub-woofers.

Subsonic overload

While the high pass analogy extends an octave or so below f_2, the extreme LF behaviour must be taken into account, since many audio systems provide considerable subsonic energy due to disc warps etc. In the case of a sealed box, the driver motion continues to decrease with reducing frequency below cutoff. The sealed box plus 3rd order element, the latter being a series capacitor, also follows this pattern. However the ported reflex systems do not. The resonant augmentation of low frequency output with reduced driver excursion relates only to the frequency range close to f_3, and at lower frequencies the port output shifts out of phase with the driver resulting in the 24 dB/octave rolloff.

In this lower range as there is very little acoustic load presented to the driver and since the air cushion of the sealed box is absent, the driver will have little motional resistance to subsonic excitation. In many domestic audio disc playing streams, the LF driver in a reflex enclosure may be seen to be in continual oscillation at subsonic frequencies thus impairing both linearity and the system power handling capacity.

It can be argued that subsonic energy should be removed by the addition of suitable filters in the amplifier, but as in practice the problem does exist, it cannot be ignored in system design.

Subjective considerations and transient response

When choosing the desired low frequency characteristic for a high performance system, subtle subjective considerations may well prove important. For example, it is known that a frequency response with a relatively high cutoff (60 Hz) and a slow rate of rolloff, (initially 6 dB/octave), may be preferable in terms of colouration and perceived bandwidth, to one where a wider response is uniformly maintained to 45 Hz, but which rolls off quickly at 24 dB/octave. Thus although from the viewpoint of an engineering specification the latter would appear to represent the ideal case, in fact, subjective judgement indicates the reverse to be true. Why this is so is not fully understood, although it may be associated to some extent with the poorer transient response and inevitable delayed ringing present to some degree with typical fourth order designs (reflex systems). The rapid phase shift as the system enters the resonance range may also be a contributing factor. Although covering a range of reduced aural sensitivity, an overall response extension to say 35 Hz seems to be more important than a flatter response with a higher cutoff. (In this lower range the output of the low rolloff rate sealed-box system will probably exceed that of the corresponding reflex case.)

High acoustic outputs

It was mentioned earlier that the attainment of high acoustic powers requires a large driver diaphragm. The greatest excursion is demanded at low frequencies where the volume of air displaced is the quantifying factor. Thus

$$V_{A_{max}} = S_D d_{pk},$$

where S_D = piston area, and d_{pk} = the allowable peak excursion. The maximum power output for a given bandwidth over the reference frequency range is given by

$$P_{max} = k_p f_3^4 V_{A_{max}}^2, \quad (k_p = \text{power constant})$$

with the drive adjusted to keep the unit's displacement within d_{pk} over the working passband. k_p depends on the spectral energy distribution in the programme and also on the system and its response shape. For typical speech and music programmes, k_p approximates to 0.85 for a closed box, and 3.0 for a reflex enclosure[10].

In the case of the 30 litre enclosure discussed earlier, let us compare the alternatives of reflex and sealed driver loadings as designed for the same cutoff frequency. If the maximum acoustic power was equivalent to 100 dB spl for the sealed box, the reflex equivalent for the same diaphragm excursion would be 105.5 dB, assuming that the driver could tolerate the increase in input power, and that non linearities in the vent were not excessive at this sound pressure level.

Air non linearity

Another potential source of distortion is the excessive compression of the air in the box. If this exceeds 5% by volume, harmonic production from the source may be significant. In practice this is unlikely to occur as the output in the case of a medium sized enclosure would be approaching a very loud 120 dB spl at one metre. If greater levels are required then it would be expedient to increase the box size. Since a larger driver with a high power rating will undoubtedly prove necessary, a larger box will in any case be employed.

Incidentally, such distortion is also a problem with horn systems, particularly high output mid range drivers where the effective air compression in the horn throat is considerable.

Compact enclosures

While it is self evident that for most applications a loudspeaker system should be as small and unobtrusive as possible, the fundamental efficiency Equation 4.1 dictates that if a given system is reduced in size, a sacrifice must be made in terms of either LF extension or efficiency. If the latter consideration is inconsequential due to the ready availability of high power amplifiers, then the bandwidth and output power may be maintained in a small box. However a stage will ultimately be reached where either:

(1)   the thermal power handling limit of the motor coil is reached, or

(2)   the non linearity of port or air volume becomes significant, or

(3)   the size of magnet system required to energise the increasingly long throw coil becomes too large and costly.

The most influential factor is undoubtedly the cutoff frequency f_3, and as the efficiency is proportional to the third power of f_3, a sacrifice in bandwidth is a logical step. Merely by moving the cutoff frequency one half octave higher, e.g. from 38 Hz to 50 Hz, the enclosure volume may be reduced by nearly 2.5 times without any significant loss of efficiency or maximum acoustic power output.

Low frequency sensitivity of the ear

Another relevant point concerns the human ear's low frequency characteristic and its maximum acoustic output.

Reference to the Fletcher—Munson hearing sensitivity curves will show the ear's poor sensitivity at low frequencies. Clearly there is no point in designing a speaker system whose response extends to 35 Hz if it cannot generate sufficient acoustic levels for these frequencies to become audible.

Taking the case of a 90 dB sound level at 1 kHz, and assuming this to be the maximum output of a certain system, suppose that the programme carries an orchestral bass drum note at 40 Hz, which appears at a level 30 dB below peak. Noting the maximum system spl at 90 dB the drum note will be reproduced at 60 dB, which is just on the threshold of perception, and hence the attainment of a 35 Hz cutoff in such a speaker with an overall 90 dB spl maximum is almost worthless. To do justice to modest level bass sounds the system spl maximum would have to be raised to at least 100 dB. This fact virtually rules out frequency responses extending below 50 Hz from compact enclosures with low maximum output levels, regardless of the miracles of engineering which are claimed to exist inside. Hence for effective low frequency performance a high quality speaker must be capable of producing an adequate acoustic output over the designed range. It is precisely because the ear's low frequency sensitivity is poor that bass musical instruments are the largest in the orchestra; their size indicative of their ability to produce sufficiently high energy at low frequencies to be heard.

Programme spectral content

The previous example citing the bass drum at 30 dB below the mid-band maximum level is not atypical, and in general the averaged bass content of normal programmes falls rapidly below 100 Hz. This implies that below this level the maximum undistorted acoustic power capability of a system may be compromised without audible deterioration. Such a concession will in fact allow a typical system possessing a cutoff at 50 Hz to be operated at a maximum overall programme level 8 dB higher than the actual 50 Hz overload point.

Alternatively, where a system is designed with bass boost equalisation in mind, there will be approximately 8 dB of available headroom at 50 Hz for equalisation, when referred to the nominal reference band power level. (When a speaker system is to be used specifically for low frequency reproduction such as a solo electric bass guitar, this headroom will need to be reduced, and the system designed accordingly[11].)

Damping

Both Thiele and Small have indicated that there should be no need for acoustic damping in a system at low frequencies[3,4]. (Absorption is of course necessary for the higher frequencies, see Chapter 7.) Generally speaking, it is only those systems which are poorly designed, often with insufficient electromagnetic damping, that require additional absorption in the form of a dense volume filling or resistive structures in the port. Such enclosures invariably have low values of k_n, the power constant; much lower than the practical values suggested earlier in this chapter. In addition, k_p, the power handling factor, is usually below optimum.

Damped systems generally reflect a designer's decision to make use of an existing driver, possibly chosen for its mid-band rather than LF properties. He then makes the best of a theoretically poorly matched driver/box combination by smoothing the resulting output irregularities through resistive damping, this is inevitably wasteful of bass power and system efficiency.

4.3 CLOSED-BOX SYSTEM

This is an attractive form of loading due to its simplicity of construction and ease of manufacture. It may be considered theoretically as an infinite baffle mounted driver with an additional stiffness component added to the existing suspension compliance, this due to the springiness of the air volume trapped in the enclosure. Clearly a smaller box will have a greater stiffness contribution than a larger one, and in sealed-box sys-

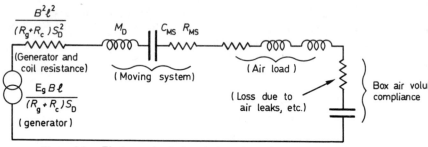

Figure 4.2   *Electromechanical equivalent circuit for a driver in a closed box*

tems this air restoring force is normally made dominant compared with that of the driver suspension.

Overmuch has been made of the high linearity and of this 'air spring' loudspeaker. In fact the air stiffness in the phases of compression and rarefaction differs, and if the volume change is significant by comparison with the total value (i.e. more than 5%), the resulting distortion may be obtrusive. Harwood states that in a typical 60 m^3 listening room, to produce a sound level of 105 dB, a sealed-box speaker with an f_3 cutoff frequency of 40 Hz must be at least 65 litres in volume, if a 3% second harmonic distortion criterion is specified. With a 10 litre enclosure and a 60 Hz f_3, the listening room sound pressure cannot exceed 96 dB[8]. In practice some additional allowance may be made for the reducing LF content of normal programme. While the larger infinite baffle speakers will certainly supply enough undistorted output for most domestic and medium level monitoring purposes, the distortion described may well prove to be a limitation for some high level IB designs.

Analysis

The complete acoustical circuit (electromechanical) for a sealed-box system is illustrated in Fig.4.2. Due to the poor efficiency of such speakers the air load impedance is very small and may be neglected. Likewise resistance losses in the cabinet (leaks etc.) may be assumed negligible. The circuit now simplifies to Fig.4.3. Here R_{AT} represents the total series resistance; M_{AC} the total mass including diaphragm and adjacent air mass, and C_{AS} the total compliance of both driver and air spring components. This acoustical circuit may be transformed into its electrical equivalent to facilitate analysis, as in Fig.4.4.

The system response is that of a damped single-resonant circuit. Two reactive components are present, hence the transfer factor $G_{(S)}$ is second order, and demonstrates a 12 dB/octave rolloff below resonance.

$$G_{(S)} = \frac{S^2 T_c^2}{S^2 T_c^2 + ST/Q_T + 1}$$

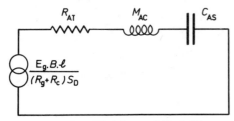

Figure 4.3   Simplified form of Fig.1 (like components are summed forming a simple tuned circuit)

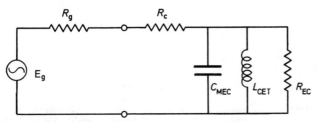

Figure 4.4   Voltage or impedance equivalent form of Fig.4.2 ($M_{AC} \equiv C_{MEC}$, $C_{AT} \equiv L_{CET}$ and R_{EC} represents the mechanical losses)

Where

$$T_c^2 = \frac{1}{\omega_c^2} = C_{MEC} \cdot L_{CET}$$

this defining the resonant frequency f_c. Since Q_T = total driver Q at f_c, for a normal low output impedance driving amplifier

$$Q_T = \frac{Q_E Q_M}{Q_E + Q_M}$$

where

$$Q_M = \omega_c C_{MEC} R_{EC}, \text{ the mechanical } Q$$

$$Q_E = \omega_c C_{MEC} R_C, \text{ the electrical } Q$$

$$C_{MEC} = \frac{M_{AC} S_D^2}{B^2 l^2}$$

$$R_{EC} = \frac{B^2 l^2}{(R_{AB} + R_{MS}) S_D^2}$$

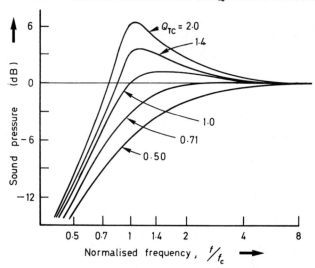

Figure 4.5   Amplitude v's normalised frequency response of closed-box loud-speaker system for several values of total system Q_{TC} (after Small). See Fig.3.24. (Note the reference levels for each case are normalised.)

Since a minimum phase characteristic is shown by the system the parameters of phase and amplitude/frequency are sufficient to describe completely its behaviour.

Response shape

Figure 4.5 illustrates the possible range of useful response shapes for a normalised cutoff frequency f_c, when Q_{TC} lies between 2 and 0.5. The latter figure corresponds to the critically damped alignment where the response is -6 dB at resonance, and the initial rate of rolloff is slow at 6 dB/octave, down to approximately half the cutoff frequency. The transient response will show no ringing and little overshoot.

The Butterworth 'B2'* is a popular alignment where $Q_{TC} = 0.7$; this places the -3 dB point at f_c. The response is maximally flat and still possesses a satisfactory transient characteristic. Putting Q_{TC} equal to unity provides a greater bandwidth since the -3 dB point appears at approximately 0.8 of f_c, but this is attained at the expense of a 1.5 dB response lift above cutoff. The impulse response possesses a noticeable overshoot accompanied by a cycle or so of ringing. Increasing values of Q_{TC} do not serve to further extend the response, and the overshoot and response peak at resonance continue to increase.

*   These and the other alignments mentioned are from Thiele[3]. These are respectively Butterworth alignment 2 and Chebychev alignment 2.

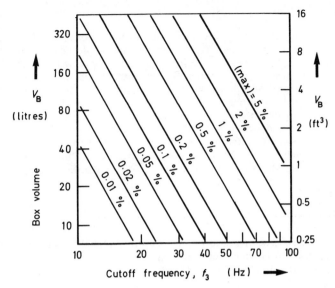

Figure 4.6   The relationship of maximum reference efficiency to cutoff frequency and enclosure volume for the closed-box loudspeaker system; f_3 is the cutoff frequency (after Small)[7]

If a 2 dB peak in the response is acceptable, this corresponding to the 'C2 Chebychev' alignment where Q_{TC} is 1.1, it results in the optimum efficiency alignment for a sealed box system, and offers a nominal 1.8 dB increase in sound pressure over the B2 alignment for the same −3 dB cutoff frequency. (In essence, the improved bandwidth of the 'C2' alignment has been traded for a higher reference efficiency.)

Enclosure value and efficiency

With the 'C2' alignment, a table has been drawn up of the maximum reference efficiencies for various box sizes. Figure 4.6 shows, for example, that the maximum efficiency even a large 120 litre sealed box enclosure can achieve is limited to 1%, for a 35 Hz cutoff frequency. If the latter were increased to 45 Hz (a not unreasonable figure) the theoretical efficiency may be seen to double to 2%.

A conventional 40 litre system with a typical 40 Hz cutoff cannot exceed 0.5% in efficiency (f_c about 48 Hz with the C2 alignment).

The section on LF equalisation in this chapter explains how the effective efficiency may be increased by choosing an over-damped alignment with a high reference efficiency, and then restoring the −3 dB, f_c point through bass lift in the accompanying amplifier, provided that sufficient headroom is available.

Box filling or damping

A volume filling may offer an apparent air volume increase of up to 15%, and additionally may add a mass component due to the physical movement of the filling at the lower frequencies. The combined effects lower the system resonance and must be accounted for in the design. With a light diaphragm and a dense but flexible filling, the effective cone mass increase may be as much as 20%. Very dense fillings will increase the frictional losses in the enclosed air volume and augment the damping. If the system is designed correctly such damping is not required, but may help to control a system where the Q_{TC} is too high, perhaps due to inadequate magnet strength. Complications arise with filling movement; for example the transfer function can differ significantly for transient as opposed to steady state excitation.

Design example

To assess its performance in a range of enclosure sizes, Small[10] examined an LF unit with the following properties: f_0 = 19 Hz; Q_m = 3.7; Q_E = 0.35; V_{as} = 540 litres and Q_T = 0.32. Using

$$\eta_0 = \frac{4\pi^2 f_0^3 V_{AS}}{c^3 Q_E}$$

the reference efficiency was found to be 1.02%.

The effective piston radius was estimated at 12 cm, so S_D = 45 sq. cm, the piston area.

The system damping is invariably less than that of the driver alone, (i.e. Q_{TC} is greater than Q_T) and the ratio of the two depends either on the ratio of the enclosure compliance to that of the driver, or alternatively on the ratio of the enclosure volume to the equivalent compliance volume of the driver. The ratio is denoted α, where $\alpha = V_{AS}/V_B$, and since the box should represent the controlling restoring force in a closed box system, α is rarely below 3. Since the response shape is proportional to the total system Q, and this depends on α, both shape and cutoff frequency for a given driver are controlled by this ratio.

Figure 4.7 shows this relationship, and alignments for the driver example are given below.

The lowest Q_{TC} (0.72) is attained with the driver using the largest enclosure volume worthy of consideration, (135 litres). Despite this Q_{TC} remains more than double the driver Q alone, (0.32), which indicates that not only should the driver compliance be high for sealed-box designs, but also the driver Q should be sufficiently low. This alignment approximates to B2 and hence f_c (the box resonance) and f_3 the −3 dB cutoff) are the same in this example, i.e. at 42 Hz, approximately twice the driver free air resonance.

A smaller 60 litre cabinet offers a compliance ratio equal to 9. The

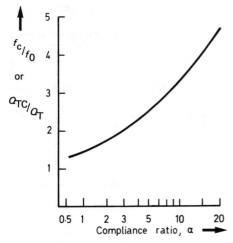

Figure 4.7   Ratio of closed-box resonance system f_c and Q_{TC} to driver resonance frequency, f_0, and Q_T, as a function of the system compliance ratio α (after Small)[7]. (Note system Q increases with α, ie reducing box size.)

system Q rises to unity with a small peak at resonance, (60 Hz), and this peak extends the -3 dB point to 47 Hz. If the cabinet volume were to be further reduced, the Q would exceed unity but could probably be adequately controlled by additional damping offered by a dense volume filling. Many drivers available on the o.e.m. (original equipment manufacturer) market are not too well suited even for sealed box use, due to their excessive Q. Many have Q_T values between 0.6 and 1 which implies that virtually any box design used with them will have an excessive system Q and a resulting rise at resonance, unless heavy damping is applied in the form of a dense volume filling and/or thick felt layer applied over the rear chassis of the driver. This resistively loads the local air movement adjacent to the diaphragm but efficiency is bound to be impaired as a result. (In his series of papers Small[4-9] comprehensively covers such total design of driver and enclosure to meet a given specification.)

4.4 REFLEX OR VENTED ENCLOSURES

The idea of venting or porting an enclosure to augment and extend its LF response by exploiting the Helmholtz resonance, is quite an old one. The first reflex patent can be attributed to Thuras and dates from 1930; since then numerous simplified and improved methods of analysis have been developed, culminating in the review of techniques presented by Small[8,9] in the early 1970s and the several computer aided design programmes that have derived from his work[14,15].

For a given engineering expenditure, venting offers the following advantages compared with a sealed box.

(1)   Greater maximum acoustic output (up to 5 dB increase for a typical programme drive).

(2)   Higher efficiency (50% or +3 dB for similar ripple free responses).

(3)   Lower cutoff frequency (30% lower with the standard 'B2' alignment).

The hybrid form using an auxiliary bass radiator (ABR) may be a little more expensive owing to the cost of the additional moving element; (with a normal reflex the extra radiating element is simply the plug of air trapped in the port or tube). The ABR method[9,27] gives a cleaner sound as the windage noises and possible pipe resonances associated with small long ports needed for compact enclosures are thereby avoided. The ABR undoubtedly extends the scope of reflex design right into the compact enclosure range traditionally dominated by sealed box enclosures.

Transient response

The fourth order, 24 dB/octave final rolloff for a reflex system endows it with a fundamentally poorer transient response than a sealed box. However, lower-than-optimum efficiency alignments such as QB3 or SC4* may be chosen, whose characteristics are quite similar to the sealed box while retaining the reduced diaphragm excursion and consequent power handling advantage of the reflex.

Opinions concerning the subjective transient response of reflex systems, may be influenced by the boomy character of the many poorly designed examples in production today many of which have Q_{TC} values greater than 3. Reference to typical room reverberation characteristics indicates that passband ripple up to 1.5 dB at low frequencies is likely to be subjectively inaudible, this criterion permitting the use of the response-extending Chebychev alignments with their higher values of system Q.

It is not implied that other acoustic systems are free of resonance mechanisms, as investigation of the upper-range transducers used in many loudspeaker designs, or alternatively the operation of a number of high performance microphones will show. In both cases, the use of controlled acoustic resonance techniques to extend and flatten the response is widespread.

Analysis

Omitting the preliminary stage by considering Fig.4.3 we may add the

---

*   These and the other alignments mentioned are from Thiele[3]. These are respectively 'Quasi Butterworth 3' and 'Sub-Chebychev 4'.

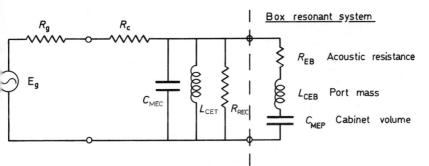

Figure 4.8   Equivalent circuit of driver and ported (reflexed) cabinet

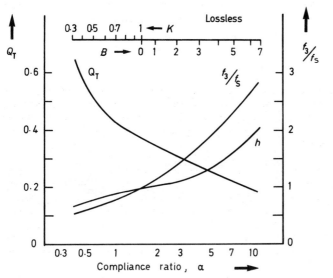

Figure 4.9   Alignment chart for lossless vented-box system

mass component of the port (ABR or air plug) to the equivalent circuit to obtain Fig.4.8. The complete ABR analysis is more complex due to the finite compliance of the passive radiator suspension.

Whereas in Fig.4.3 the enclosure compliance was combined with the driver, in this case a separate circuit is necessary, comprising the addition of the enclosure port resonance, the total forming a fourth order, high-pass network. As with the closed box case, the compliance ratio

$$\alpha = \frac{C_{AS}}{C_{AB}} = \frac{L_{CES}}{L_{CEB}}$$

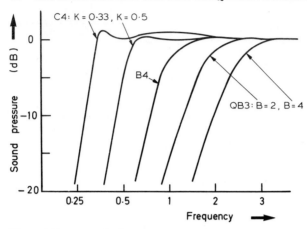

Figure 4.10   Normalised response curves for B4 and selected C4 and QB3 align-ments of vented-box loudspeaker system (after Small)[8].   (B4 maximally flat Butterworth)

The full derivation is beyond the scope of this book, and system en-gineers are recommended to follow the references quoted[3,4]. Small's alignment chart for the basic C4, B4 and QB3 alignments is given in Fig.4.9, with the accompanying responses, Fig.410.

To a first approximation the enclosure losses may be neglected; (high losses are caused by badly leaking cabinets or a theoretically un-necessary volume filling of absorbent). On the chart the values of k and B specify the 'C4' and 'QB3' alignments. f_B is the Helmholtz resonance of the enclosure; f_0 is the driver free air resonance; h is the tuning ratio equal to f_B/f_0 and Q_T is the total driver Q.

Design example

Example of driver vented enclosure design for 300 mm frame size driver. The data given is: f_0 (f_S) = 30 Hz Free air resonance; B = 1.2 T Flux density; Bl = 12 Wb/m Force factor; R_c = 6 Ω Motor coil d.c. resis-tance; $S_D = 5.5 \times 10^{-2}$ m^2 Diaphragm effective area; $M_D = 4.5 \times 10^{-2}$ kg Diaphragm mass; R_{MS} = 3 Ns/m (mech Ω) Suspension resistance; Airload = 10^{-2} kg (both sides).   Now

$$Q_E = \frac{2\pi f_0 M_T R_c}{B^2 l^2} = \frac{2\pi \times 30 \times 5.5 \times 10^{-2} \times 6}{12^2} = 0.43$$

$$Q_M = \frac{2\pi f_0 M_T}{R_{MS}} = \frac{2\pi \times 30 \times 5.5 \times 10^{-2}}{3} = 3.5$$

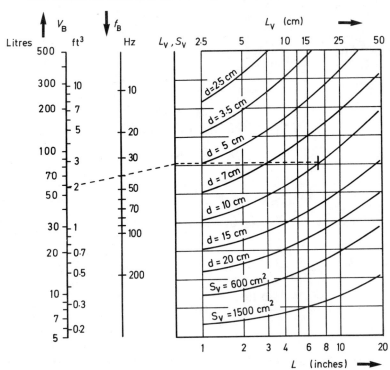

Figure 4.11 Nomogram and chart for design of ducted vents (after Small)[8].
(f_B = enclosure resonance, L_v = vent tube length and S_v = vent area, no tube required)

and

$$Q_T = \frac{Q_E Q_M}{Q_E + Q_M} = \frac{0.43 \times 3.5}{3.93} = 0.38$$

For a maximally flat response, $\alpha = 1.4$ (Table 11 of Reference 16), $h = 1.2$ and $f_3/f_0 = 1.30$, approximately. Now the enclosure volume

$$V_B = \frac{V_{AS}}{\alpha}$$

where

$$V_{AS} = C_{AS}\rho_0 c^2, \qquad C_{AS} = C_{MS}S_D^2$$

and

$$C_{MS} = \frac{1}{f_0 \times 2\pi M_T}$$

so that

$$V_B = \frac{\rho_0 c^2 S_D^2}{\alpha f_0^2 \times 2\pi M_T} = \frac{1.18 \times 345^2 \times 5.5 \times 10^{-4}}{1.4 \times 30^2 \times 2\pi \times 5.5 \times 10^{-2}}$$

$$= 0.097 \text{ m}^3 \ (\hat{=}100 \text{ litres})$$

Now $f_B = hf_S = 1.2 \times 30 = 36$ Hz, $f_3 = 1.3 \, f_0 = 39$ Hz. From the nomogram (Fig.4.11) a ducted port 10 cm diameter by 10 cm long is appropriate.

The reference efficiency

$$\eta_0 = \frac{4\pi^2 f_0^3 V_{AS}}{c^3 Q_{ES}}$$

$$= \frac{4\pi^2 \times 30^3 \times 0.136}{345^3 \times 0.43} = 0.82\%$$

Vented-box distortion

Harwood has investigated typical situations and shown that for a 60 m^3 listening room, to produce realistic sound levels of 100–105 dB with an f_3 in the region of 40 Hz, the distortion from quite small vents of 5 cm and upwards in diameter will not prove subjectively obtrusive[12].

It has been suggested that the use of an ABR can reduce the distortion at high powers and can also block the egress of standing wave energy from within an enclosure at higher frequencies. With large boxes the internal absorption can be very effective; an accompanying reasonably sized vent offers negligible colouration and distortion, and may well be capable of higher maximum acoustic output than the ABR. It is worth noting that the precise area of an ABR is almost immaterial; the high volume velocity of a well designed vent may exceed that of a practicable ABR by several times, and the expression 'increased radiating area' as applied to an ABR is misleading. Ultimately the reflex system will be limited by the non linearity of the air volume in the cabinet, in the same way as with a sealed box.

For a given vented enclosure quite striking improvements in subjective and objective performances may be achieved by improving the smoothness of airflow in the vent. The velocity of air in the vicinity of a port may be very high, well over the value required to produce turbulence and this is particularly troublesome with the smaller ports below 5.0 cm in diameter.

In some cases the use of a tube helps by allowing an increased port diameter but these are drawbacks, with Harwood indicating that a length to diameter ratio of more than 2:1 is inadvisable. Fluid flow theory indicates one immediate difficulty with 'tunnel ports' namely that the ease of air flow is greater for the input or enclosure volume compression part of the cycle than the output or expansion part. This is because on the first the air flow is essentially from a hemisphere over the front panel down the tube, whereas in reverse, the internal air stream approaching the exposed end of the port tunnel is divided reducing the local pressure gradient and thus the volume flow. In consequence over a few cycles of low frequency drive in the region of enclosure resonance a net increase above atmospheric pressure is built up within the cabinet. Distortion, already produced by this rectification mechanism, is now further augmented as the back pressure pushes the driver diaphragm out of its linear working flux region.

With small ports, two practical ideas have been tried with significant measureable improvement. One consists of streamlining the important edges, for example for a simple aperture the inside and outside edges may simply be radiused. One model showed a 40% improvement in distortion at 50 Hz at a nominal power level by the addition of a soft polyurethane foam liner, 12 mm thick in a simple port opening. Under stroboscopic examination its mode of action was found to be one of turbulence damping, the port liner edge moving with and thus controlling the 'windage' particularly reducing the higher 'chuffing' harmonics (this addition due to Spendor).

Bose have developed quite sophisticated port design in a small reflexed enclosure using fluid flow theory to establish a complex moulded streamlined form. Others have tried related methods such as a matrix of fine parallel pipes in the tunnel to aid laminar air flow. These are often realised as packed straws or a moulded honeycomb structure.

Computer aided design

A paper by Rank Wharfedale engineers is particularly relevant to this field of study[14] and sets out the following basic criteria for any system design, namely:

(1) Sensitivity; (dB per watt at one metre or, volts into 8 Ω)
(2) −3 dB cutoff frequency
(3) Cabinet size or volume
(4) Response shape or alignment, (including damping and driver impedance considerations).

A particular set of values cannot be arbitrarily assigned to these criteria owing to their interdependence, and the main objective in using a computer is to generate many sets of possible alignments which may be easily inspected for useful combinations.

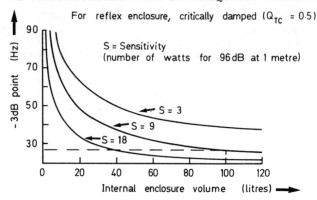

Figure 4.12
Sensitivity: 86.0 dB at 1.0 m for 1.0 W input
System internal volume = 100.0 litres
Bass cutoff frequency 26.8 Hz
Bass unit parameters:

EL	V	FS	Unit	Power	(BL) 2/RE	mms	cms
−23.0	100.0	26.8	130.0	50	0.0	0.0	0.0
−23.0	100.0	26.8	170.0	50	0.0	0.0	0.0
−23.0	100.0	26.8	200.0	50	7.16	16.6	21.1
−23.0	100.0	26.8	250.0	50	17.49	40.6	8.7
−23.0	100.0	26.8	300.0	50	0.0	0.0	0.0
−23.0	100.0	26.8	380.0	50	0.0	0.0	0.0

RE(1.1.1.1) = 000000
RE(10,3,5,2) = 10.5361
The above extract follows insertion of data and shows two viable solutions: the
one chosen is the 250 mm driver with a 50 mm pole, a moving mass of 50 g and
a compliance of 8.7 × 10.4 m/N. The $(Bl)^2/RE$ refers to the driving force devel-
oped in the voice coil and magnet assembly and imparted to the cone.   The
programme continues to give details for the driver such as correct sizes for the
magnet, the wire, top plate, throw, and the number of coil layers and turns

The design information required of the programme is summarised as
follows:
(1)   An indication of the range of theoretical solutions.
(2)   An indication of the possible practical solutions.
(3)   An indication of the relative costs of (2).
(4)   Quantitative results to enable practical values to be assigned
       to the variables in the system design equations.
(5)   Quantitative details of driver parameters, e.g. moving mass,
       compliance, free air resonance, etc.
A programme was then devised based on the established LF loading
equations to generate the required data.
From the results obtained, curves could be drawn up relating the
various parameters and hence allowing the rapid choice of useful solution sets (Fig.4.12).

A further computer programme also deriving from the papers of Thiele and Small was published by the AES in the early 1970s[14,15] and many manufacturers are actively pursuing the various other aspects of computer aided design; for example, the fast Fourier transform analysis of loudspeaker impulse responses (see also Reference 23).

LF alignments, equalisation and motional feedback

It has been indicated on the section on LF loading that certain alignments may require equalisation. For example, take the case of the optimal system response in Chapter 3, Fig.3.27. If a +6 dB increase in efficiency were required, this obtained by doubling the magnet strength, the system would then be overdamped and require equalisation. Reference to the alignment pertinent to the new system will show the degree of bass lift necessary. In this case, the initial slope is 6 dB/octave, which may be applied at the input of the matching amplifier. An additional rolloff is desirable below the system cutoff frequency, so that overload at subsonic frequencies does not occur as a consequence of the otherwise continuing equalisation.

The degree of equalisation which may be applied is dependent on the spectral content of the programme employed, together with consideration of the excursion and thermal rating of the LF driver.

The converse equalisation is also possible; i.e. correction of an underdamped response. This is achieved by either a suitable 'dip' network ahead of the amplifier or alternatively by adjusting the output impedance of the amplifier to a negative value at low frequencies, thus increasing the overall electromagnetic damping[24,25].

The sixth order alignment may be exploited to produce new performance standards for a given enclosure size. Keele[25] and Stahl[24] examine the classic Theile analysis on vented enclosure design with reference to the 6th order alignments, these relying on an auxiliary 2nd order filter usually ahead of the power amplifier. Theile's B6 alignment 15 is chosen on which to base a new set of alignments, which allow a much wider choice of driver compliance. The 2nd order auxiliary filter applies a boost to the power input to the vented enclosure system and the whole provides high acoustic output with minimal diaphragm excursion, Fig.4.13.

Both high compliance and low compliance drivers are amenable with suitable choice of alignment, if necessary with some passband ripple.

Stahl[24] has shown how 6th order alignment may be applied to the design of a sub-woofer, the latter referring to an enclosure added to an existing pair of speakers which provides an octave or two of extreme bass often missing from smaller full range systems. Stahl extends the concept of utilising an amplifier with a negative output resistance to control loudspeaker Q by introducing a complex negative impedance at the amplifier terminals connected to the loudspeaker, Fig.4.14. This

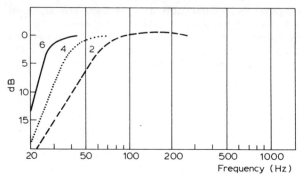

Figure 4.13   Low frequency performance of a 300 mm frame, high compliance LF unit with f_0 = 22 Hz, Q_{ES} = 0.28, V_{AS} = 414 litres; '2' is the second order response in a 40 litres closed box, −3 dB at 63 Hz; '4' is the 4th order QB_3 response in a 114 litre vented box with box tuned to 33 Hz, −3 dB system response at 33 Hz; '6' is the 6th order response, same cabinet as '4' but tuned to 26 Hz and with 2nd order bass lift, −3 dB point now 26 Hz (after Keele)

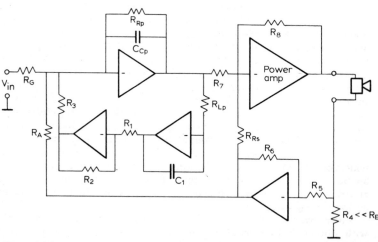

Figure 4.14   Realisation of ACE-Bass amplifier useful for experiment purposes (after Stahl)

$$R_s = \frac{1}{R_{Rs}} \; \frac{R_4 R_6 R_8}{R_5} \quad C_p = C_{Cp} \frac{R_A R_5 R_7}{R_4 R_6 R_8} \quad R_p = R_{Rp} \frac{R_4 R_6 R_8}{R_A R_5 R_7}$$

$$L_p = R_{Lp} \frac{R_1 R_3 C_1}{R_2} \; \frac{R_4 R_6 R_8}{R_A R_5 R_7} \quad G = \frac{1}{R_G} \; \frac{R_A R_5}{R_4 R_6}$$

dominates the characteristics allowing electrical control of the apparent mechanical characteristics of the connected driver, enabling the designer to utilise existing drivers and synthesise an exact desired alignment. An example is quoted[24] where a 20 Hz, −3 dB response was required from a 50 litre cabinet at 100 dB, 1 m (2π) at 5% or less distortion. Two special 170 mm drivers in push pull were used which possessed a high force factor and large excursion.

The required mechanical parameters were synthesised via the amplifier impedance characteristic, and involved a moving mass increase from 38 to 260 g, damping from 26 to 58 kg/s and a compliance reduction from 0.45 to 0.25 mm/N. The reference band efficiency remains unchanged, at the high level set by the drivers themselves.

The idea of motional feedback[17] is not a new one and dates from the 1930s. Recently it has resurfaced in several commercial designs, these incorporating modular transistor power amplifiers, where the convenience of the latter as compared with the earlier valve units must be a major contributing factor. The driver moving system is coupled to a sensor that generates a signal which may be fed back to the power amplifier, and can be used to correct any motional error or non-linearity. The error signal will only be valid as long as the cone is operating as a piston, and hence in general the correction can only be operative over the lower octaves. At very low frequencies the correction must be rolled off so that the unit is not driven out of its allowable mechanical excursion limits, and in consequence, feedback is only possible over a specified bandpass. Within this range, however, the driver non-linearity may be considerably reduced, both in terms of pressure response uniformity and distortion, this technique allowing poor quality, high resonance LF units to produce remarkable results in very small, sealed enclosures. Notwithstanding, the colouration problems associated with such enclosures still remained.

It is important to place the technique in its proper perspective. The compensation of major deviations in response through feedback involves equally large power demands to meet the deficiencies. A typical example employs a 280 mm driver in a 20 litre box, with an under-damped system resonance at approximately 110 Hz. The unequalised response at 35 Hz is more than 18 dB below the reference level, the latter specified at 200 Hz. While the application of motional feedback results in an f_3 point at 35 Hz, a 120 W amplifier is needed to achieve this, even taking into account the reducing headroom requirements at the lower frequencies. While the distortion of this example is under 2% from 40 Hz to 200 Hz, at 93 dB, 1 m, there is little evidence that distortion values of less than 5% at these lower frequencies are essential, even for a high performance speaker. Furthermore, if this driver example had possessed reasonable linearity the equalisation could have been equally performed by a simple bass boost network in the driven amplifier, which would probably have resulted in a similarly satisfactory subjective result. Low efficiency is the penalty to be paid for extended bass response in small boxes. An efficient unit in a compact enclosure will require consider-

Servo loudspeaker system - layout

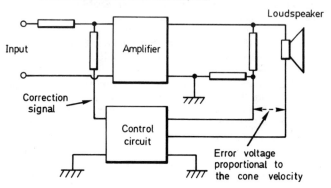

Figure 4.15   A feedback system utilizing the variation in motional impedance. Alternatives include cone motion sensing accelerometers (courtesy Servo Sound)

able equalisation to achieve a wide uniform response. Consequently, in both the cases of equalisation and feedback, a similarly high-powered amplifier will be required.

The only significant technical advantage of motional feedback lies in the improved amplitude linearity, but in any case, LF distortion would not appear to be much of a problem with conventional, well designed loudspeakers. While it is certainly true that poorly engineered systems may be 'rescued' by a feedback arrangement, when overload does occur it manifests itself with greater severity than in a non-feedback system. This can be an important consideration when a loudspeaker may be subject to occasional overload on loud programme transients.

Technically most feedback designs employ an accelerometer attached to the diaphragm, the former usually concealed beneath an enlarged dust-cap. Its output is electrically processed and fed in anti-phase to the accompanying power amplifier (Fig.4.15).

While other pickup transducers including magnetic and electrostatic types have also been proposed, a version of the latter has in fact been employed in a system recently launched in West Germany. Motional feedback is applied to all the drivers over their respective piston ranges; the piston bandpasses are wide since the mid and treble is handled by dome units and the bass by an array of four closely coupled, 100 mm cone drivers (Fig.4.16).

4.5 TRANSMISSION LINE ENCLOSURES

In theory a transmission line or labyrinth is capable of being extended to infinity, providing a perfectly resistive termination to the driver by absorbing all the rear directed energy. Hence in this respect it may be

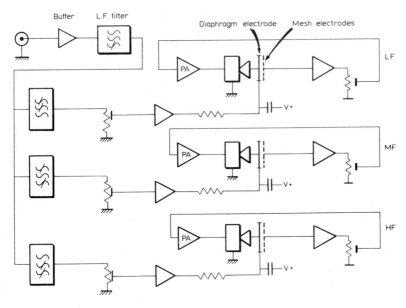

Figure 4.16 General system of 'Monitor 8'. Metallised diaphragms are polarised at V_+ = 400 V. Capacitive electrostatic pickup via mesh electrodes spaced in front of diaphragms. Incoming filtered signal mixed with error signal from electrode and fed to power amplifiers as control signal for correction of frequency response and linearity (after Backes and Muller)

regarded as a special case of a very large sealed box, which is itself the practical realisation of an 'infinite baffle'.

Physically the line resembles an acoustic pipe which, in its folded form, is also known as a labyrinth. The cross-section must be sufficiently large in order that the rear-directed energy is not impeded, and yet it must also be long enough to terminate the energy down to the lowest desired frequencies. Since the path length must be comparable to the wavelength absorbed, if genuine low frequency reproduction is the aim, ideal transmission lines quickly become overlarge, even when folded. For a given closed line, the absorption reduces as the cutoff frequency is approached. This means that the energy is beginning to be reflected back to the driver and the system will then approximate to a sealed box of the same total volume. For example, a filled absorptive line intended to operate effectively down to 35 Hz must be at least 8 m long. If a cross-section of 30 cm^2 is adopted, (roughly equivalent to that of a 36 cm diameter bass driver) then the enclosure volume will be inordinantly large at 720 litres.

Practical lines are of necessity smaller in cross-section to reduce the total volume, and pipe resonances and reflections at the higher frequencies may become a problem unless the absorption is very carefully arranged. It was discovered by Bailey that a filling composed of long-haired sheep's wool at a density of 8 kg per cubic metre possessed better acoustic properties compared with other materials, such as glass fibre. More specifically, at low frequencies (30—60 Hz) the speed of sound in the line appears to be reduced by 50%, which has important implications[18,19].

While in theory a damped line is a perfect absorber, and the termination at the far end is of no consequence; it may be closed or open, in practice, commercial designs invariably leave the line open. Energy propagated below the line's cutoff frequency will emerge from the aperture and depending on its phase will augment or cancel the main contribution from the front of the driver. Over a limited range of frequencies such an enclosure will behave as a reflex, the propagation delay down the line providing the required phase inversion. This is where the wool filling comes into its own, since for a given length of line the delay is effectively doubled, thus lowering the cutoff frequency of the system as a whole.

It has been suggested that the mechanism of this increased delay is at least partially due to the air velocity in the line reducing at low frequencies, due to the movement of the wool mass. As such, the latter represents an inertial component in the energy path down the line, thus accounting for the delay.

A further effect at low frequencies is produced by the air mass in the line moving with the driver, and this component is additive to the driver's own moving mass. Whereas in conventional boxes the air mass is quite low, often less than 20%, in an open transmission line the mass addition may be equal to that of the driver itself, thus reducing the latter's loaded resonant frequency by a factor of $\sqrt{2}$.

Two main resonant modes are possible in this conventional type of open pipe, these occurring at ½ wavelengths and at odd (as opposed to even) multiples of the effective quarter wavelength. Taking the example of a 2 m filled pipe with moderate absorption, (packing density below 5 kg/m^3) the quarter-wave mistermination occurs at about 30 Hz and the half-wave mode at 73 Hz. If the pipe is overdamped, too much energy will be absorbed, and the sound output will possess a gradual rolloff from as high as 70 Hz. In commercially viable systems, i.e. those of reasonable size, it is difficult to find a satisfactory compromise between a uniformly extended LF response and an upper bass/lower mid-performance with minimal colouration-inducing line resonances (Fig.4.17).

Finally, the performance achieved with a transmission line is often no better than that of a properly designed reflex enclosure of similar dimensions. In fact for the same expenditure the results from the reflex sub-class the ABR, may even be superior. Currently transmission line speakers are characterised by lower than average efficiency, not withstanding their large size.

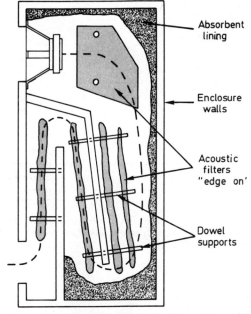

Absorbent
lining

Enclosure
walls

Acoustic
filters
"edge on'

Dowel
supports

Figure 4.17 Practical transmission line enclosure (internal volume ≃100 litres for f$_c$ at 35 Hz). (Courtesy IMF)

4.6 HORN LOADING

The specialised subject of horns can only be briefly covered in this book, and interested readers are again referred to the bibliography for more detailed information[21]. While the author is aware of the danger of generalisation on this subject, in his view, horn loaded enclosures are not capable of top class subjective quality, and most designs are much poorer than typical direct radiator systems. The main reason for adopting horn loading, traditionally employed in public address situations, is to attain a high efficiency coupled with an improved control of directivity, both vital considerations when large audiences are to be covered.

Improved acoustic matching

The intrinsic low efficiency of direct radiator diaphragms is due to their poor matching to the acoustic impedance of the air load. Almost any value of acoustic impedance may be produced at a horn throat by suitable geometrical design, and thus the match to the driver diaphragm may be optimised. Two benefits result; one, the efficiency is greatly increased and two, resistive termination presented to the diaphragm may greatly reduce the amplitude of any intrinsic response irregularities.

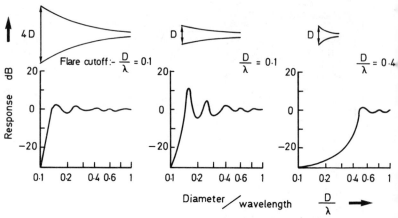

Figure 4.18   Typical response frequency characteristics of horn loudspeaker for different mouth openings and different flare cutoffs as function of the ratio of the mouth diameter to the wavelength (after Olsen)[22]

Efficiency

While optimum magnet design together with horn matching can result in efficiencies of nearly 50% in narrow band designs, if the frequency range is increased, great difficulty is experienced in maintaining both a smooth response and a high efficiency. A full multiway horn system capable of 40 Hz to 20 kHz over a useful $60°$ forward polar response, potentially may have an efficiency in the 10–20% range, but in practice this is often much less.

Bandwidth

The greatest problem is physical size. For a simple horn the lower cutoff frequency* is proportional to the effective diameter of the mouth when radiating into free space (i.e. 4π steradians). The mouth area = $\lambda_c^2/4\pi$ where λ_c is the cutoff wavelength. For example, for an f_c at 40 Hz, the mouth area should be 5.9 m^2. Such a design would need to be custom built into a location as part of a fixed structure, and is clearly impractical for most domestic situations. Figure 4.18 shows the influence of horn proportion and size.

The response may be extended in two ways. A small closed box may be added which loads the rear face of the diaphragm and provides an inductive impedance component. This may be adjusted to offset the increasingly capacitive throat impedance below cutoff. Additionally, if the radiation space is reduced, e.g. by mounting the system in a wall

* The frequency at which the acoustic impedance becomes reactive rather than resistive, i.e. the resistive component has fallen by 6 dB.

(2π) or between a wall and floor (π) or in a corner $(\pi/2)$, the impedance match improves proportionately. Effectively, the flare of the horn is extended by the adjacent wall surface thereby reducing the cutoff frequency. With corner mounting a bass horn may have an basic mouth area $1/8$ that of the free space mounted version, since the effective radiation space is reduced from 4π to $\pi/2$.

Position

Certain problems will arise if a horn is mounted in a corner. Maximum excitation of the room LF modes is inevitable, these producing irregularities in the radiation impedance and consequently in the sound pressure. In addition there will be mid-band colouration as the reproducing assemblies cannot always be flush fitted to the adjacent walls; this being virtually impossible with three way horns.

Propagation delay

Propagation delay in a horn produces large phase displacement which complicates the crossover points in a multi-way system. In theory the mouths should be aligned such that the propagation time to the listener from all energising diaphragms is the same, but the necessary physical displacement of the assemblies is impractical. However, the recent development of electronic delay lines of satisfactory quality means that the mouths of multiway horns may now be conventionally aligned to the designer's convenience, and the differential delay and resulting phase discrepancy may be electronically compensated. The resulting system must of course be powered by separate amplifiers with active filter crossovers.

Folded horns

Theoretically a horn structure should be linear, and the smaller mid and treble types do adopt this format. However large bass horns (15 m or more for a free field model) require some folding technique, unless the horn can be concealed; for example, built into the sub-floor structure. If the folds are too severe, reflections will occur, resulting in irregularities in the throat impedance, and hence the frequency response.

Horn shape

Basic horn flares include the exponential, hyperbolic and tractrix forms (Fig.4.19). The relationship between the cross-sectional area of an exponential horn and the axial distance x from the diaphragm is given by

$$S = S_0 e^{mx}$$

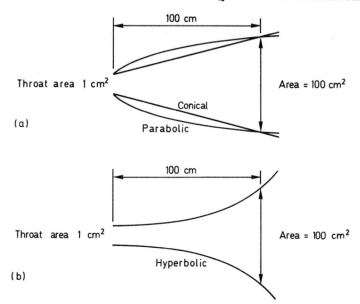

Figure 4.19   *(a) Longitudinal sections of conical and parabolic horns. (b) Longi-tudinal sections of a hyperbolic horn (from* Acoustics *by L. Beranek, Copyright 1954. Used with permission of McGraw-Hill Book Co.)*

and the cutoff frequency by

$$f_c = \frac{mc}{4}$$

where S = cross-section; S_0 = throat cross-section = distance from throat; m = flare constant and c = velocity of sound.

The hyperbolic horn offers a short flare for a given cutoff combined with good driver termination, although the throat distortion is fairly high for a given output level. Horns with combinations of exponential, conical and hyperbolic profiles have also been used, the results largely depending on the empirical skill of the designer and the method of construction.

Directivity

The variable geometry of horn shapes has been taken even further by recent commercial designs where in an effort to maintain a constant horizontal directivity over a wide frequency range, the horn may be 'flattened'. The resulting mouth resembles a radial flared slot. Alternatively the horn may be 'thinned' in the vertical plane to strengthen the diffraction radiation effect to give good dispersion in the lateral plane.

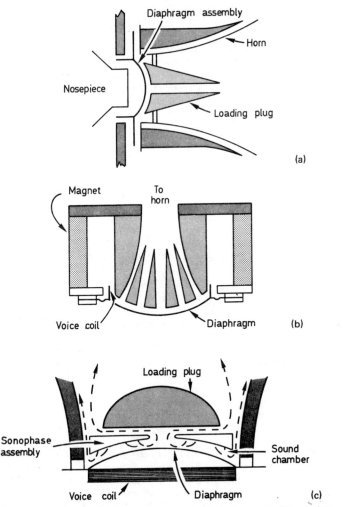

Figure 4.20   Examples of phase plugs used in the throat of HF horns (diagram (c) after Electrovoice)

In addition to the well known multi-cell methods, acoustic lenses and diffraction plate structures are also commonly employed to disperse the energy.

Upper range problems

The lower range cutoff has been discussed but a high range cutoff will also be present, this due to a combination of several factors. The driver diameter is of significance, as in a simple horn, where the throat is directly coupled, an upper frequency cutoff exists where the dimensions of the throat cavity are comparable with a sound wavelength. One solution involves reducing the throat cross-section considerably, and in addition, fitting a multi channel coupling block in the remaining acoustic space. This places the throat-cavity resonance at a higher frequency, but eventually breakup will limit the maximum working frequency of a given diaphragm.

Figure 4.20 illustrates various throat structures which smooth and extend the response. An unfortunate by-product of reducing the throat section is a rise in the throat pressure change at lower frequencies, thus increasing the distortion. In part, this explains why it is impossible to design a single, wide range horn capable of high quality performance.

Commercial horn systems

Many high output commercial systems employ horn loaded mid and treble transducers where the resulting high efficiency endows the design with a considerable power handling capacity. The LF range is usually a compromise, and generally employs a parallel combination of two or three 300 mm−350 mm high power, coned bass drivers in an optimum reflex enclosure. The latter will utilise a high efficiency response alignment which incorporates bass lift equalisation in the accompanying power amplifier.

Efficiencies of the order of 5% are possible using this technique and acoustic outputs of the order of 125 dB at 1 m are obtained with the energy maintained over a 60° forward arc up to at least 15 kHz.

The subjective performance is not on a par with direct radiator monitoring systems, but these horn designs are very satisfactory for their prime application, namely large audience sound coverage.

REFERENCES

1. Harwood, H. D., 'Speakers in corners', *Wireless world,* 162, April (1970)
2. Allinson, R. F., 'The influence of room boundaries on loudspeaker power output, *J. Audio Engng Soc.* 22, No.5, 314−9 (1974)
3. Thiele, A. N., 'Loudspeakers in Vented-Boxes', Pt.1, *J. Audio Engng Soc.* 19, (1971): Pt.2, 19, No.6 (1971)
4. Small, R. H., Synthesis of Direct Radiator Loudspeaker Systems, (University of Sydney)
5. Small, R. H., 'Simplified loudspeaker measurements at low frequencies', *J. Audio Engng Soc.* 20, No.1. (1972)
6. Small, R. H., Direct radiator loudspeaker system analysis, *J. Audio Engng Soc,* 20, No.5 (1972)
7. Small, R, H., 'Closed-box loudspeaker systems', Pt.1, 'Analysis', *J. Audio Engng Soc.* 20, No.10 (1972), Pt.2, 'Synthesis, *J. Audio Engng Soc.* 21, No.1 (1973)

8. Small, R. H., 'Vented-box loudspeaker systems', Pt.1, 'Small signal analysis, *J. Audio Engng Soc.* 21, No.5 (1973), Pt.2,'Large signal analysis', *J. Audio Engng Soc.* 21, No.6 (1973), P.3, 'Synthesis', *J. Audio Engng Soc.* 21, No.7 (1973), P.4, 'Appendices', *J. Audio Engng Soc,* 21, No.8 (1973)

9. Small, R. H., 'Passive radiator loudspeaker systems', Pt.1, Analysis, *J. Audio Engng Soc,* 22, No.8 (1974), Pt.2, 'Synthesis', *J. Audio Engng Soc,* 22, No.9 (1974)

10. Small, R. H., 'Direct radiator loudspeaker system analysis', *J. Audio Engng Soc.,* 20, No.5 (1972)

11. Harwood, H. D., 'Loudspeaker distortion associated with low frequency signals', *J. Audio Engng Soc.,* 20, No.9 (1972)

12. Harwood, H. D., 'Non linearity of air in loudspeaker cabinets', *Wireless World,* 80, No.1467 (1974)

13. Small, R. H., 'Closed box loudspeaker systems', Pt.2, 'Synthesis', *J. Audio Engng Soc.,* 21, No.1 (1973)

14. Gelow, W. J. and Rhodebeck, M. G., 'The scientific design of a three-driver loudspeaker system', *Proc. A.E.S. 46th Convention* (1973)

15. Garner, A. V. and Jackson, P. M., Theoretical and Practical Aspects of Loudspeaker Bass Unit Design, *Proc. A.E.S. 50th Convention,* London, March (1975)

16. Small, R. H., 'Vented-box loudspeaker systems', Pt.3, 'Synthesis', *J. Audio Engng Soc.* 21, No.7 (1973)

17. Harwood, H. D., 'Motional feedback in loudspeakers', *Wireless World,* 80, No.1459, p.51 (1974)

18. Bradbury, L. J. S., 'The use of fibrous materials in loudspeaker enclosures', *J. Audio Engng Soc.* 24, No.3 (1976)

19. Bailey, A. R. 'Non resonant loudspeaker enclosure', *Wireless World,* October (1965)

20. Bailey, A. R., 'The Transmission Line Loudspeaker Enclosure', *Wireless World,* May (1972)

21. Dinsdale, J., 'Horn loudspeaker design', *Wireless World,* 80, No.1459, 1461, 1462, (1974) These articles include a comprehensive bibliography on the subject.

22. Olsen, H. F., *Modern Sound Reproduction,* Van Nostrand Reinhold, New York (1972). Copyright 1972 by Litton Educational Publishing, Inc.

23. Adams, G. J., 'Computer-aided loudspeaker system design', Pt. 1 and 2, *J. Audio Engng Soc.* 26, No.11 and 12 (1978)

24. Stahl, K. E., 'Synthesis of loudspeaker mechanical parameters by electrical means', Preprint 1381 (K-3), *61st Audio Engng Soc. Convention* (1978)

25. Werner, R. E. and Carrell, R. M., 'Application of negative impedance amplifiers to loudspeaker systems', in *Loudspeaker Anthology* (Cooke, R. E. Ed.) *J. Audio Engng Soc.* 1–25 (1979)

26. Keele, D. B., 'A new set of sixth order vented box loudspeaker alignments', *J. Audio Engng Soc.* 23, No.5 (1975)

27. Fincham, L. R., 'A bandpass loudspeaker enclosure', *63rd Audio engng Soc. Convention* (1979)

28. Holl, T., 'Engineering the AR9', Teledyne Acoustics Research (1978)

29. KEF Electronics Ltd., 'Model 105', *Keftropics,* Issue 3, No.1 (1978)

BIBLIOGRAPHY

Benson, J. E., 'An introduction to the design of filtered loudspeaker systems', *J. Audio Engng Soc.* 23, No.7 (1975)

Beranek, L., *Acoustics,* McGraw-Hill, London (1954)

Cooke, R. E. (Ed.) *Loudspeaker Anthology, J. Audio Engng Soc.,* 1—25 (includes References 2, 3, 5, 7, 8, 18 and 25) (1979)

Hanna, C. R. and Slepian, J., 'The function and design of horns for loudspeakers', *J. Audio Engng Soc.* 25, No.9 (1977)

Harwood, H. D., 'New B.B.C. monitoring loudspeaker', *Wireless World,* May (1968)

Harwood, H. D., 'Some aspects of loudspeaker quality', *Wireless World,* May (1976)

Henrikson, C. A. and Ureda, M. S., 'The Manta Ray horns', *J. Audio Engng Soc.* 26, No.9 (1978)

Hilliard, J. K., 'A study of theatre loudspeakers and the resultant development of the Shearer 2-way horn system', *J. Audio Engng Soc.,* 26, No. 11 (1971)

Hoge, W. J. J., 'A broadcast monitor speaker of small dimensions', *J. Audio Engng Soc.,* 26, No.6 (1978)

Keele, D. B., 'Sensitivity of Thiele's vented loudspeaker enclosure alignments to parameter variations', *J. Audio Engng Soc.,* 21 (1973)

Kloss, H. E., 'Hoffman's iron law', *Hi fi Sound*

Long, E. M., 'Design parameters of a dual woofer loudspeaker system', *Proc. A.E.S. 36th Convention* (1969)

Rank Leak Wharfedale, *Airedale SP Loudspeaker,* Press Release

Lord Rayleigh, *Theory of Sound,* Dover Publications

Walker, P. J., 'Wide-range electrostatic loudspeakers', *Wireless World,* May, June and August (1955)

Wente, E. C. and Thuras, A. L., 'Auditory perspective loudspeakers and micro-phones', *J. Audio Engng Soc.* 26, No.718 (1978)

Zacharia, K. P., 'On the synthesis of closed-box systems using available drivers', *J. Audio Engng Soc.,* 21, No.9 (1973)

5

Moving-coil direct radiator drivers

In contrast to the theoretical analysis presented so far, this chapter covers the practical aspects of moving-coil driver design. The techniques employed in high performance models are described, with critical review where appropriate. Inevitably some overlap of content with theoretical subjects — driver analysis, low frequency loading, etc. will occur, but essentially the viewpoint taken here is a practical one.

As has been mentioned elsewhere, moving-coil drivers are used in the vast majority of loudspeakers. There is a great variety of chassis, magnets and coils available, as well as numerous diaphragm shapes and materials to choose from, and thus several classes of specialised drivers covering individual frequency bands have been developed.

It has also been indicated that a single full range driver cannot as yet satisfactorily meet the requirements of a high performance reproducer At its simplest, the latter must be 'two or more way', i.e. incorporating at least two drivers, each responsible for separate adjacent frequency ranges, which together with an enclosure and crossover from the complete system. Several categories of drive unit may be broadly classified as in Table 5.1.

After a short review of the essentials of the moving coil transducer, drivers with coverage approximating to these bands will be individually examined.

5.1 MOVING-COIL MOTOR SYSTEM

The heart of a moving-coil driver is the motor, which consists of a light, hollow coil immersed in a strong radial magnetic field, suspended in such a way as to allow free movement only in the axial direction.

Some sort of diaphragm or radiating surface must be attached to the motor coil to couple the air to the forces generated by currents flowing in the coil, and hence to permit acoustic power (i.e. sound energy) to be radiated from the assembly.

97

TABLE 5.1

Useable frequency range	Type of driver
30 Hz–1 kHz	Low frequency (LF)
30 Hz–5 kHz	Low to mid frequency (L/MF)
150 Hz–5 kHz	Mid frequency (MF)
700 Hz–10 kHz	Upper mid frequency
1 kHz–20 kHz	Upper mid/treble frequency
3 kHz–20 kHz	High frequency (HF)
8 kHz–30 kHz	Very high frequency (VHF)

Every component in a moving-coil driver unit has some influence on the quality of the sound produced, whether it be in terms of pressure response, level, distortion, colouration, frequency response or directivity. Some may influence certain aspects only; for example, a lack of uniformity of the magnetic field may affect the distortion at a certain sound pressure level; without significantly altering any other aspect of the performance. Changes in the strength of the magnetic field, however, will alter both output and frequency response, the latter due to the variation in electro-magnetic damping factor near the fundamental resonance (see Fig.3.27, Chapter 3).

The main components in a moving coil driver are illustrated in Fig.5.1, a cross-section of a cone model. The corresponding form for a dome unit is shown in Fig.5.6.

The diaphragm or sound radiating element

This may vary in diameter from 12 mm to 50 cm and may be formed in a variety of shapes and profiles, ranging from domes to cones, both convex and concave.

The surround or outer support

Found in cone units and comprising the flexible structure joining the cone rim to the chassis. Most dome drive units do not have a separate surround, the edge suspension often being the only means of support for the main structure.

The suspension or inner support

Usually found near the join between the motor coil and the diaphragm, this rear support member is a concentrically corrugated fabric disc joining the cone apex to the chassis. The function of both the suspension and the surround is to allow relatively free axial or piston movement

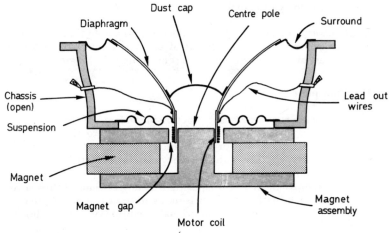

Figure 5.1   Moving coil driver components

of the diaphragm whilst offering great resistance to lateral displacement or rocking motion of the diaphragm.

The motor coil (or voice coil)

This is an assembly consisting of a shallow coil wound on a light, hollow tube firmly attached to the diaphragm. Flexible leadout wires convey power from the amplifier to this coil.

The magnet

This usually refers to the complete magnet assembly which provides a strong uniform radial magnetic field through the motor coil. This is the polarising field against which the alternating fields produced by the coil act, resulting in mechanical force on the moving assembly.

The chassis (or supporting basket or frame)

The chassis is usually a separate pressed steel or cast framework which provides a rigid foundation for all the other components, and a means by which the driver is fitted to an enclosure. In some dome high frequency units, the front magnet plate alone provides all the functions of the chassis.

The dust cap or centre dome

As the name suggests, this element does not usually fulfill any acoustic function and merely keeps dust out of the gap. However, it may be an integral part of the acoustic design in some units.

The phase plate

This may be a partial acoustic obstruction in the front of the diaphragm, or it may be a short horn-like structure adjacent to the dome. Its function is essentially that of equalisation. Irregularities of sound pressure, directivity or phase with frequency may be corrected, particularly in dome diaphragm units.

The design of all these components is strongly related to the driver application, (i.e. the frequency it is designed to cover) and as such the details will be included in the individual discussion of driver types that follows.

5.2 LOW FREQUENCY OR BASS UNITS

Low frequency design is intimately associated with the enclosure or loading method employed (see Chapter 4). A driver intended for high performance applications will possess a level reference region above the fundamental resonance. The total Q of such a driver is likely to be below unity and its actual value is a vital factor in determining the design of the enclosure, whether sealed or reflex. For example, a sealed box system Q greater than unity implies a significant hump at resonance, a condition likely to be unacceptable for a high performance system.

As shown in Fig.3.27, the system Q for a given motor coil resistance and winding length is predominantly controlled by the flux density in the magnet gap. For any given driver there is an optimum value of magnet strength for the maximum level output. Greater efficiency may be achieved at the expense of low frequency extension, and/or by increasing the volume of the enclosure.

Since bass drivers essentially operate as pistons, the acoustic power generated at a given frequency is proportional to the area of the cone and its peak excursion, i.e. the volume of air actually 'pumped' by the diaphragm. For each halving of frequency the required excursion for constant power is doubled, and for a given power and driver size, one can quickly reach a low frequency limit at which the driver ceases to operate linearly due to limits of available cone movement. The latter may be due to suspension constraint and/or the coil movement exceeding the region of constant magnetic flux.

In the case of the infinite baffle or more correctly 'sealed box' enclosure, once limits are set for the cone size and matching enclosure volume as well as for tolerable non-linearity the resulting response must

(a)

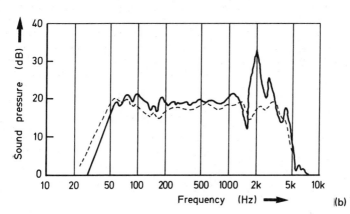

(b)

Figure 5.2   (a) A 'sandwich' cone 380 mm LF driver.   (b) Typical response curves, with and without nodal mass loading control

be a trade-off between low frequency extension and efficiency. This is why small, wide-range loudspeakers are inevitably inefficient.

Diaphragm materials (LF)

While designers hope that bass drivers operate as pistons, this is rarely the case over the entire frequency range. Attempts have been made to reproduce highly rigid structures; Celestion, KEF Electronics, Yamaha and Leak have all employed reinforced polystyrene diaphragms in various forms. While Leak employed a cone, the 'Sandwich', the others utilised solid structures. An aluminium foil coating on both sides of the diaphragm provided reinforcement (Fig.5.2). Resonances in such rigid diaphragms are difficult to control, but the major problem concerns the fact that when such a stiff structure does enter breakup, the effects may be severe, and the more gentle breakup of an ordinary diaphragm is generally preferred in applications where the driver must be used in or near the breakup range.

An established example of a reinforced polystyrene bass driver is the B139, manufactured by KEF Electronics (Fig.5.3). The unit operates as a pure piston up to approximately 800 Hz, where the first breakup mode occurs. It is used successfully in a number of current high performance systems, ideally with a high slope crossover at 200—300 Hz, although some designers have worked up to 450 Hz. The radiating area approximates to that of a 250 mm diameter circular unit and the model has been employed for both large reflex and compact sealed box designs.

In the effort to combat the weaknesses of conventional paper/pulp cones, other formulations have also been tried. EMI developed an elliptical laminated structure comprising a reinforced glass fibre layer bonded to a conventional cone. A further development consisted of two stiff cones laminated with a flexible damping layer between the two. Thick pulp cones formed under low compression are also favoured, since their high internal damping lowers colouration. Technics have developed a three layer, pulp cone material for their advanced bass drivers, consisting of stiff outer layers with a soft centre layer of high damping.

Other manufacturers have sought to increase the rigidity of conventional cones by the addition of some high strength matrix such as carbon fibre. Sony, Pioneer and Son Audax are all actively researching this aspect.

While the developments mentioned so far have enjoyed reasonable success the honours must undoubtedly go to a synthetic isotropic cone material marketed under the name of 'Bextrene', and consisting of a mixture of polystyrene and neoprene. Well designed cones made from this material, if suitably terminated by an appropriate surround and appropriately coated with a PVA* such as Plastiflex, offer a low/mid frequency performance well in advance of other cone types. Not only

* Aqueous suspension of polyvinyl acetate.

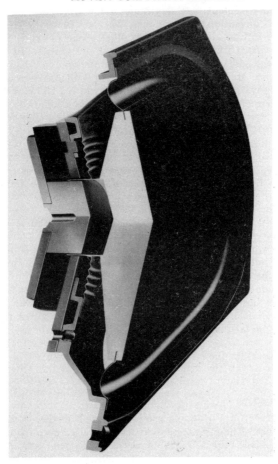

Figure 5.3   An expanded polystyrene wedge diaphragm, with stressed aluminium skin (courtesy KEF Electronics)

is the fundamental 50 Hz to 500 Hz range covered in almost textbook fashion, but the favourable characteristics of low distortion and colouration plus excellent response uniformity may continue for several octaves above, making the choice of crossover points and slope less critical.

The BBC engineers who pioneered the use of this material succeeded in producing a two way high performance monitor system with a 300 mm LF/MF driver crossing over at 1.7 kHz [1].

At the time of writing a successor to Bextrene has emerged, which on listening and laboratory tests appear to offer the same order of magnitude of improvement over Bextrene, as the latter demonstrated with respect to conventional paper cones. This new plastic is based on polypropylene, with an added mixture of polyethylene of molecular weights and mix chosen for the optimum acoustic properties. In addition, it possesses the additional advantage of requiring no extra damping, as the internal losses are intrinsically sufficient. In similar thicknesses to those employed for Bextrene drivers (25—37 micron for 200 mm drivers, and 37—65 micron for 300 mm units), the cone mass is reduced resulting in a sensitivity improvement of the order of 100% for the same driver assembly. Doubts exist concerning consistency. Recently Wharfedale have obtained more promising results from a homopolymer polypropylene, chalk filled. By selection of constituent mix and grade both stiffness and internal damping may be enhanced, with better consistency.

As with Bextrene, the performance of a well designed 300 mm driver made from polypropylene is satisfactory to beyond 2 kHz, and has allowed the completion of a second generation two-way system based on the BBC example quoted above. The response curve of the new driver is smooth and well balanced up to 4 kHz (Fig.5.4). The commercial system in which it is employed (Chartwell 450) uses a complex active equaliser, but the equalisation is more concerned with compensation for enclosure diffraction effects than driver anomalies.

Metal cones have also been produced but usually by the time resonances have been controlled, the efficiency is reduced due to the high mass. In addition, as with the rigid polystyrene structures, the breakup modes in metal diaphragms can be severe. Nevertheless, aluminium diaphragms are in use by several manufacturers, one employing expanded foam metal for the LF unit, and another a honeycomb structure.

Other materials that have been tried include polyethylene, both solid and expanded, and unplasticised p.v.c. and many others.

Diaphragm shape

Some of the effects of diaphragm shape have been discussed in Section 3.1 on cones. These principles cannot be ignored even for bass drivers, and the determination of a suitable profile for a given material and driver size is to a large degree a matter of trial. The choice of surround is vital, and strictly speaking, the surround is best considered as a continuation of the diaphragm even though it is a separate component generally made from a different material.

With vacuum formed thermoplastic cones, the best result to date have been given by flared, moderately shallow profiles. The transition between the neck and the motor-coil former should form a smooth curve, and to inhibit 'folding over' of the edge, the tangential angle between the cone rim and front plane should not be much less than 25°.

The flare rate, cone and motor-coil diameter, coil mass and cone thickness will all affect the linearity, slope, range and directivity of the pressure response. Even if a bass driver is not intended to operate beyond 400 Hz, it is worth designing the unit to give a well behaved characteristic at least two octaves above, since this will generally reduce colouration and the crossover transition will be better defined.

(a)

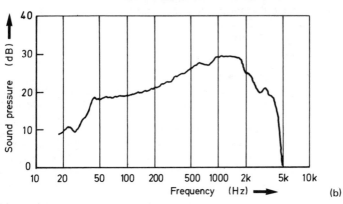

(b)

*Figure 5.4   (a) A 305 mm polypropylene cone LF/MF driver.   (b) Typical
unequalised response curve showing extended, well controlled characteristics
(courtesy Chartwell Electroacoustics)*

Surrounds

This component is important to all drivers but it is most critical in low frequency applications, where it must perform two roles.   Firstly it must provide a large amplitude excursion at low frequencies with a resistance to the considerable attendant differential air pressure, and simultaneously, give effective absorption and termination of energy at the cone edge through to the mid-range. It must also support the cone for years at a time without sagging.   In the past, surrounds were generally formed by a series of concentric corrugations, either as an extension of the cone edge or an additional component.   By contrast, almost all quality drivers today employ some form of half-roll surround.   These are satisfactorily linear and can be made to the high compliance values required for low resonance sealed cabinet drivers.   In addition they may be formed from a variety of materials some of which offer excellent termination properties.   The curved shape of a roll-surround endows it with a resistance to the high differential pressure between the front and rear sides of a bass driver under strong LF excursion.   Materials which overload gradually give less distortion, and plastic foams and rubbers are greatly preferable to treated cambric or similar doped fabric.   Although they are quite heavy, surrounds of moulded neoprene are extensively used with bass drivers (Fig.5.3), and recently other related substances such as nitrile rubbers, and the lighter material, highly plasticised p.v.c. have also proved satisfactory.   The latter was also found to be particularly suitable for mid range applications due to its excellent termination properties.   Hitachi have patented a new type of pleated surround of doped fabric offering improved excursion linearity and termination.

Foamed plastics are also used (noteably polyurethane), which may have additional doping applied on the inside surface.

Historically there have been many problems associated with attaching certain surround materials to cones, but modern adhesives, if correctly chosen, are generally satisfactory.

Some manufacturers are successfully using RF heating methods to bond plastic surrounds to plastic cones. This method has the advantage of eliminating the danger of cone distortion due to softening when solvent based adhesives are employed.

Designers must take into account the divergent requirements, namely good dissipation of vibrational energy above 150 Hz or so; a profile which allows reasonably linear excursion up to 8 mm peak to peak, and a mechanical structure which inhibits self resonance.   In a particular prototype driver, a response dip occurred at about 600 Hz, whose source was eventually traced to an anti-resonance in the p.v.c. surround. A flat section had been designed between the half roll and cone edge, but another was unintentionally present between the outer 'roll' edge and the clamping point on the chassis. The unwanted circuit comprised the 'roll' vibrating with the compliance of the two adjacent flat sections. Readjustment of the roll dimension to eliminate the outer flat portion removed the dip.

Suspensions (LF)

The compliance of synthetic surrounds is usually temperature dependent; a p.v.c. type may vary by two-to-one over a range of $15°$ to $30°$C. A low frequency driver will often need a reasonably stable fundamental resonance, e.g. for a reflex loaded application. The surround of such a unit, if temperature sensitive, clearly should not provide the bulk of the diaphragm restoring stiffness. The latter must then be dependent on the remaining supporting component, namely the suspension.

Good quality suspensions are manufactured from a polyamide fabric (nylon or polyester) impregnated with a cured, temperature stable epoxy resin. If carefully designed, the suspension can provide a stable restoring force over the required excursion.

The suspension should also be engineered so as to limit gently at the peak displacement allowed by the magnet assembly. This will reduce the severity of coil jump-out effect noted in the section on magnet/coil systems in Chapter 3, p.53.

It is also possible to control the suspension non-linearity by suitable choice of material and geometry, to compensate for the magnetic non-linearity produced by large excursions[2]. This is important if an optimal efficiency, short-coil short-gap assembly is used, where the coil length is only 5—10% greater than the physical magnet gap. Some of the BBC Bextrene driver systems employ this technique, but owing to the difficulty of its execution, the newer generation of reflex loaded monitors have reverted to a more conventional linear suspension and employ a motor coil with an approximately 25% coil overhang.

Poorly designed suspensions, particularly those which are large and heavy, may possess self resonances at only a few hundred Hz. Additionally, poor quality cotton or linen fabric suspensions fitted to heavy coned bass drivers can take a 'set' away from the nominal centre zero coil position in a matter of days, particularly under humid conditions and if the units are stored horizontally. Vertical positioning relieves the suspension of the axial bias due to gravity, but the long term stability is still in doubt.

In practice, any suspension may develop a degree of off-centre 'set' if stored in one direction long enough, which is why vertical mounting, particularly of heavy coned bass drivers, is strongly recommended.

Double suspensions (LF)

While there is little evidence that moderate degrees of suspension non-linearity are audible at low frequencies, some manufacturers have attained very low orders of bass distortion by utilising a double suspension. The corrugation geometry is arranged to be complementary, so making the excursion characteristic identical in both the forward and the reverse directions.

With large drivers intended for high power applications, the lateral forces at the voice coil may be sufficient to cause momentary decentering. A spaced double suspension may then be used to advantage, resulting in a greatly improved resistance to decentration.

Motor coil and magnet assembly (LF)

The moving diaphragm mass for a given unit size is virtually a fixed quantity. The motor coil diameter is generally proportional to its thermal power handling, and with these two factors decided, the efficiency of the resulting driver is proportional to the square of the magnetic field strength in the gap. The design of magnet structure will depend on the loading and maximum undistorted output requirements for the system. For example, take the case of a sealed box with a long throw 200 mm driver, which is required to develop 96 dB from 60 Hz upwards. Suppose it possesses a magnetic field strength acting on the coil length immersed in the gap sufficient to provide a system Q of about 0.7. Since a large cone excursion is demanded to produce 96 dB at 60 Hz, about ±6 mm peak, a typical 6 mm magnet gap will require a coil overhang of at least twice this, resulting in a total coil length of approximately 18 mm. An unavoidable loss in motor efficiency occurs, since only one third of the available power in the coil is actually used in creating acoustic power.

It is worth noting that if the response of this system was required to extend one octave lower to 30 Hz at the same power level, the excursion must be multiplied by four, i.e. to a ridiculous 50 mm peak to peak. Sound power is proportional to the square of the diaphragm amplitude, and if undistorted reproduction down to 30 Hz is required of this particular driver, the overall power level must be reduced by 4^2 or 12 dB.

If a similar sealed box capable of 96 dB at 30 Hz were required it could be achieved within a sensible excursion limit by increasing the diaphragm size, since the power radiated is proportional to the square of the product of the moving area and excursion. If the same ±6 mm excursion is adopted, then the diaphragm area must be four times greater to radiate 96 dB at 30 Hz. Thus the required driver diameter needs to be increased to 380 mm.

Reflex loading may allow a given driver a produce more bass. The peak excursion of the LF driver at resonance is reduced by as much as four times with the technique, which allows the motor coil to be reduced in length, in turn giving a great improvement in efficiency. The resulting increase in Bl factor is in fact essential to control the working Q of the resonant reflexed system. Typically a sound pressure increase of four times (6 dB) is possible with a given driver when optimised for reflex loading as compared with sealed box. This holds true even for the same low frequency cut-off, although the reflex enclosure volume is likely to be larger than the sealed box equivalent.

Taking into account the average spectral energy distribution of programme, a well designed reflex enclosure with a 305 or 350 mm bass driver can produce upwards of 115 dB of wide band programme at 1 m; (a factor of 6 dB or so is gained by the falling energy in most programmes below 70 Hz). Higher levels may be attained by multiple arrays of such enclosures or by horn loading, although the latter technique is unavoidably bulky at low frequencies, and its use is generally restricted to fixed installations such as cinemas etc.

Power dissipation (LF)

Motor coil diameter is roughly related to cone size and power rating, with 20—25 mm coils the rule for small 100—170 mm drivers; 25 to 37 mm coils in 200 and 250 mm units, and 44—100 mm diameters for 250—380 mm units. There is no obvious acoustic advantage for large diameter voice coils, except perhaps the argument that a large voice coil on a small cone means that no part of the cone is very far from the driving point, which is likely to result in a stiffer structure unlikely to breakup until a higher frequency range is reached.

The large 75 to 100 mm coils will dissipate up to 200 W of continuous thermal power if constructed of suitable high temperature formers such as aluminium foil or Nomex, and utilising matching heat-cured adhesives.

Since most loudspeakers are at best only a few percent efficient, the bulk of the input power is dissipated as heat in the motor coil. Surprisingly high temperatures (up to $200°C$) may be developed under heavy drive, and even with models designed for domestic use, some manufacturers aim at short term service temperatures of the order of $250°C$. Several factors must be taken into consideration when temperature rises of this magnitude are to be accommodated. The increase in d.c. resistance is appreciable and will provide some degree of self limiting with regard to the maximum power drawn from a given source. It will also add a degree of non-linearity, depending on the thermal time constand of the motor coil.

King describes an example of a 305 mm driver equipped with a 75 mm coil and designed for use with an electric guitar[3]. The coil reached a steady $270°C$ after four hours running at a voltage level equivalent to 200 W into 6 Ω, the latter being the driver's nominal 'cold' specification.

The 'hot' impedance was found to be double, indicating that the driver was in fact only drawing 100 W from the source to maintain this temperature. The thermal time constant for the coil was 15 s, (the time for a 34% drop in resistance).

Clearly operation which results in an average power much above 75 W would be inappropriate for this driver, and the example highlights an often neglected problem encountered with high power units. The best method of cooling a coil is via conduction to the magnet structure. This is aided by a narrow gap clearance, a condition difficult to achieve with LF drivers as the coil excursion is considerable. However there are some ways round this particular problem. For example, the magnet gap may be made longer than the coil so that the latter is always in close proximity to a large mass of metal. Alternatively, the coil may be wound on

Figure 5.5   Example of a high temperature working motor-coil assembly. The coil is wound on alloy foil, bonded to a ventilated 'nomex' former (high temperature polyamide). Heat cured adhesives are employed (Courtesy KEF Electronics)

a large heat conducting former such as anodised aluminium foil, this helping to spread the heat over a larger area. Thirdly, the magnet/coil structure may be ventilated such that cold air is continuously pumped through the gap where the unit is under drive, thus providing forced cooling; this artifice is only effective at low frequencies, for example, below 200 Hz where the cone excursion is appreciable. The magnet structure itself may be fitted with blackened radial fins on the exterior surface to aid heat dissipation.

A further problem concerns the effect of conducted heat on the diaphragm. While the high temperature components of the motor coil may be readily designed to withstand the stress, some thermoplastic cones readily soften at around 100°C and a hot coil will quickly become decentred or detached. Even pulp cones may char at the neck and suffer from premature aging or disintegration. A solution is provided by the use of a non-conducting coil former section adjacent to the cone, which isolates the hot section of the coil from the cone (Fig.5.5).

Ferrofluids

A recent development from the USA is the use of a new fluid which may be applied to the magnet gap of moving coil drivers. It consists of a stable, inert organic diester base containing a colloidal, and hence non-settling dispersion of ferromagnetic material[4].

The liquid is sufficiently magnetic to remain firmly trapped in the regions of greatest field strength, i.e. the gap. It is thus self locating upon injection into the gap on either side of the voice coil. It may be obtained in a range of viscosities from 3,000 to 50 centipoise, with 100 cp suggested as suitable for low frequency drivers.

Interesting performance gains result from its application. In LF terms, the primary benefit is a greatly improved short term power dissipation for the motor coil, since the fluid exhibits good thermal conductivity, many times that of the air it replaces. While drivers in low power applications would derive little advantage from its use, the high power examples described might gain a short term power handling increase of up to three or four times. If additional damping is a design advantage the fluid can provide this, through choice of a suitable viscosity. Finally, the fluid provides a lowered reluctance path in the gap which reduces magnetic fringing and will marginally increase efficiency, by up to 0.75 dB, depending on the driver construction, and may also reduce distortion.

By maintaining lower coil temperatures the fluid can dramatically reduce the power compression effect noted earlier in connection with high temperature rise. Some extra centring force is also provided by the tendency for the fluid to form a uniform layer around the pole, and this may eliminate the need for additional centring, for example, via a second suspension, or may obviate the suspension altogether in a light mid-range diaphragm assembly. With heavy excursions the fluid may not flow laminarly resulting in an asymmetric distribution which may impede motion and reduce linearity. Another consideration is the catastrophic failure of the fluid when overheated.

Winding techniques (LF)

Coils may be wound with a variety of conductors, but the most common is enamelled copper. Anodised aluminium is also used, more especially in HF units where the reduced coil mass and inductance (its higher resistivity allows fewer turns) is beneficial to response extension.

Ideally, the mass of a copper coil should fill the gap to provide maximum utilisation of the available magnetic flux. In practice, a clearance must be provided for to prevent rubbing as the coil moves and to allow for change in coil former profile with age and thermal stress. A further loss occurs due to the wasted space in the winding and the thickness of the former on which it is wound.

If a rectangular cross-section wire is employed, then the space utilisation factor may be improved, with a resulting 15 to 20% increase in efficiency. The cost of these 'edge wound' coils is high and the technique is uneconomic except for a few expensive designs. Alternatively the wire may be partially deformed either before or after winding to 'square' the profile and hence reduce the air space (Fig.5.6).

A further solution requires the use of conducting insulated foil, flat wound. Such a coil would have a low inductance which might prove advantageous.

Figure 5.6   Edge-wound motor-coil using ribbon conductors

At present, the vast majority of motor coils are wound in insulated copper which may be precoated with a thermosetting adhesive to aid bonding. Most high frequency coils are heat cured to bake out any solvents or moisture which might cause bubbling or mechanical distortion in service. The majority are two layers, though four is quite common and six have been used in some short coil, long throw LF drivers. The main consideration is mass. The long coils required for sealed box units, if wound in four layers, will be sufficiently heavy to curtail the response in the mid band to possible 1 kHz or lower, and may also undesirably affect the coil mass/cone resonance. In addition, multi-layer coils are likely to have a higher inductance which may further restrict the response.

Linearity and magnets (LF)

At low frequencies, below 150 Hz, distortion is a function of loading and available excursion, both mechanical and magnetic. In the midband other factors also assume importance; for example, eddy currents in the poles. Lamination of the pole faces or the use of a special material of high permeability and low electrical conductivity around the gap will control eddy effects, and in a typical driver may reduce the distortion in the 200 Hz to 1 kHz band from 1 or 2% to below 0.25%.

Magnet poles are often operated in saturation since this gives some control of magnet strength variations, but by definition, it is also wasteful of flux. Saturation also places a limit on the maximum flux density in the gap. The usual mild steel pole and top plate allows maximum values around 1.4 T for a 25 mm pole and 1.7 T for a 50 mm pole. The incorporation of a higher saturation material for the pole faces such as Permendur or alternatively laminated permalloy, will allow a gap flux increase. Using Permendur gap components, 1.9 T has been reported in a commercial HF unit having a 19 mm pole.

Demagnetisation (LF)

While the choice of magnet material (Alnico, Alcomax, Magnadur, Cera-mag, Feroba) is usually dictated by the cost for a given pole structure, one other point also deserves mention. If a permanent magnet is stressed, either mechanically or magnetically, it tends to loose some magnetic strength. While ceramic types are exceedingly difficult to demagnetise, the iron alloy based materials are less so. Drivers employing the latter type of magnet may be unsuited to high power applications where the peak coil flux is considerable. King cites the example of a driver fitted with a long, four layer coil 37 mm in diameter, with an alnico cup magnet structure. 25 W of drive at 50 Hz resulted in 2 dB mid band efficiency drop. The worst demagnetisation effect occurred when driven in the frequency range of greatest excursion, i.e. fundamental resonance, particularly with long multilayer coils. A two layer coil under the same conditions gave only a 0.5 dB loss[5].

The dust or centre cap (LF)

The dust cap may influence the performance of LF units though its effects are usually more noticeable at mid frequencies. Functionally it prevents the ingress of dust to the magnet gap and may allow the differential air pressure at the pole to equalise that in front of the diaphragm. Conventional caps are made from porous treated fabric and contribute little to the acoustic output. However, a few diaphragms are fitted with rigid pulp/paper or even aluminium caps, where a small ventilation hole may be present at the apex. The function of such a rigid cap is twofold. The dome structure may be an additional radiating element to extend the frequency range; it may also serve as a stiffening structure helping to reduce cone breakup, particularly of those modes which tend to distort the motor coil from a circular to an elliptical shape.

Mass control ring (LF)

Occasionally reference is found to a mass control ring on a LF driver. This usually comprises a rigid metal ring attached to the diaphragm at the apex, which can be used to improve performance of certain drivers in the following way. Suppose an ideal cone for a given design of driver is too light for its required purpose, for example, a wide range, low resonance application, and mass needs to be added. Simply increasing the cone mass by substituting a thicker material will alter its acoustic properties. Instead, the mass is added as a ring weight at the neck. Additionally the ring may provide some stiffening, and in one example, the mass ring is attached via a viscous adhesive and is used to control a dominant concentric mode resonance (see Fig.5.2).

Chassis (LF)

With motor coil/magnet gap clearances of the order of 10 μ, and large LF driver magnets up to 10 kg in weight, a rigid and stable chassis is essential both for long term stability and to prevent mis-alignment due to transport shock. If properly deployed, both die-cast alloy and pressed steel are suitable materials for chassis construction.

The designer must compromise between the maximum window area at the chassis rear and the quantity of material to provide the required structural strength. Too much material produces cavities behind the cone which may colour the output; too little will encourage chassis resonance. Long, thin walled chassis sections are obviously weak structures and may resonate. A number of units have suffered from such resonances, usually in the 200 to 600 Hz range, caused by the magnet wobbling on a weak frame, and best results have only been produced when the enclosure is fitted with bracing to reinforce the chassis of such a driver.

5.3 LF/MF UNITS

The majority of smaller loudspeaker systems today are two way, and incorporate a combined bass/mid range driver plus a high frequency unit, with a crossover point at 2—4 kHz. The main driver must satisfy two possibly conflicting requirements, namely a clean, well dispersed and uniform mid-band, together with a low distortion bass with adequate power capacity.

Only in exceptional cases such as the 305 mm polypropylene driver mentioned earlier, can the larger LF units offer an adequate performance in the crucial mid-band. In this instance there is still an inevitable sacrifice in terms of narrowed directivity near the crossover point, (approximately 1.7 kHz).

The almost universal choice of chassis diameter for a wide range driver is 200 mm. Such a unit offers an unique combination of virtues, which accounts for its popularity in medium level domestic applications. If well designed, the bass power is sufficient for most domestic purposes, and an adequate bass output can be achieved in an acceptably small enclosure (20—40 litres). The frequency response and dispersion may be satisfactorily maintained up to a usefully high crossover point, generally 3 kHz. The sensitivity and power handling are both sufficient for quite demanding use without excessive expenditure on the magnet structure and with careful control of the important design factors, a genuinely high performance may be attained. (See Fig.8.31.)

Diaphragms (LF/MF)

The extension of the working range to meet an HF unit requires that the diaphragm be particularly well controlled and consistent, since it will almost certainly be operating in breakup at the higher working frequencies.   To attain a satisfactory performance, consistent uniform cone materials such as moulded thermoplastic are almost essential.

Drivers for LF/MF duty range in size from 100 mm to 305 mm although the LF power handling is obviously much reduced with the smaller diaphragms.   Mid range drivers are in fact often designed to fulfill two purposes; to act either as a true midrange unit in the more elaborate system designs, or else a bass/mid unit in the simpler enclosures.   Similarly, the larger, wide range units (200 mm and above) may often be employed in sophisticated systems for LF duty only, where their inherent low colouration characteristics are beneficial to the quality of the system as a whole.

Suspension and surrounds (LF/MF)

Little needs to be said about these two components except that the suspension is less influential in the mid-range, while the surround and its terminating efficiency become more critical as the cone enters the inevitable breakup modes.

Motor coil (LF/MF)

Whereas a long heavy coil may be a necessary requirement for an LF unit, a satisfactory extension of response to cover the mid-range may dictate a compromise whereby the coil is reduced in mass and inductance and hence shortened.   Where this is impossible to effect due to the need to maintain bass performance, the costly solution of a short, light coil immersed in a long magnet gap can be adopted.

5.4 MID-FREQUENCY UNITS

True mid-frequency units are characterised by a relatively high fundamental resonance, 100 Hz to 500 Hz as opposed to the LF driver range of 15 Hz to 60 Hz. The required excursion is small, and hence the motor coil and magnet may be optimised for maximum efficiency. Both dome and cone diaphragms are in common use, the former generally restricted to the upper frequency range (800 Hz to 6 kHz), while the latter may operate from 250 Hz to 5 kHz. The small diaphragms are generally less than 160 mm in diameter and typically range from 60 to 100 mm. Dome units smaller than 44 mm are more correctly classed as 'low treble' drivers.

The mid-range, typically 250 Hz to 5 kHz, is undoubtedly a most critical band. This is the region where the ear's sensitivity and analytical ability are most acute, and it additionally includes the greatest concentration of information in normal programme material. Many brave attempts to produce a high performance system have been unsuccessful because the designer has failed to adequately appreciate these facts. Critical listeners may tolerate moderate problems in the LF or HF bands but cannot forgive inaccuracies in the mid-range, whether they be in the form of spectral imbalances, response irregularities, distortion or colouration.

For this reason, MF units must be designed with care and used with considerable skill and judgment. It has been indicated in Section 6.1 on systems and crossovers that a reasonable response extension outside of the required bandpass is desirable to maintain smooth crossover transitions. Considering our ideal bandpass of 250 Hz to 5 kHz, we should add an octave to either extreme, this resulting in an overall mid-driver ideal bandpass of 125 Hz to 10 kHz. In the author's view, only a cone diaphragm is capable of approaching this performance. Where a high quality, moderately sized LF unit is to be used in conjunction with a mid range driver the lower crossover point may be lifted to the 600 Hz range or above, making possible the use of a dome unit. There remains, however, some reservation concerning the placement of a crossover point with its attendant polar and phase anomalies, since these occur almost in the centre of the mid range.

Diaphragm (MF)

As has been suggested, dome units give their best results in the upper mid-range and cone units in the lower range.

Domes (MF)

Their use is fashionable at present, due to an illogical belief that a dome radiates sound over a wider angle than a cone of the same diameter. In fact, the converse may be true, since in the degenerate condition, a dome approximates to an annular radiator whereas the cone approaches a point source, i.e. that formed by the smaller apex area.

The fact remains that dome units are popular among designers, and are also relatively easy to manufacture. A number of models employ press-formed fabric domes, impregnated with some suitable viscous damping material, usually synthetic rubber based. The combined suspension/surround is contiguous with the dome surface, with a small annular recess often provided for the direct attachment of the motor coil assembly. A felt plug is usually fitted just beneath the dome to absorb most of the rear radiated energy. They range in size from a nominal 37 mm to 85 mm diameter, with a variety of surround and profile shapes. Most, however, approximate to a shallow spherical section.

Their structural rigidity is poor and most of the so called 'soft' domes are in fact in some form of breakup from an octave or so above the fundamental resonance.   Incidentally, the latter may range from 250 Hz to 500 Hz.   The large surface damping component gives these drivers an almost resistance controlled acoustic characteristic, but due to the unavoidable hysteresis effect of a rubber based damping compound, they may not sound as transparent as their smooth frequency characteristics would indicate.   The better examples utilise a rather tougher diaphragm and damping material in an effort to maintain piston operation to higher frequencies.

Dome mid-units often sound 'coloured' and two factors can be held responsible for this effect.   The fundamental resonance is both relatively high and often inadequately damped as large dome units require large and costly magnet systems for optimum performance.   Poor crossover design may result in a further weakening of the control of the main resonance, this obtruding in the system sound as subjectively perceived colouration.

A complete contrast is presented by the 'rigid' domes employing diaphragms of high strength-to-weight ratio, such as dense card, titanium, beryllium, certain plastics and more recently, boron-coated metal.

With these diaphragms the structure is designed to be so light and rigid that breakup does not occur at all within the required bandpass.   The most spectacular of these designs are undoubtedly those formed in beryllium which though difficult to manufacture, offer startling gains in rigidity versus mass[5].   The Yamaha 88 mm beryllium dome unit is an outstanding example of the art, and provides virtually pure piston operation from 400 Hz to nearly 12 kHz.   This results in great clarity, though when the unit does enter breakup it does so rather more aggressively than soft domes, due to the intrinsically low damping of the diaphragm material.   It should be noted that very high strength to weight ratios may result in off-axis response irregularities due to the coincidence effect, this caused by the high sound velocity in such a diaphragm compared with normal materials.

Other promising constructions include fabric impregnated with cured phenolic resin, and mylar, the latter improved by lamination with another plastic such as p.v.c., which has a high internal loss.   Hard pulp/paper domes are also employed.

As has been explained in Section 3.1, on dome diaphragms, the profile and size is largely dependent on the chosen material.   The more rigid domes (metal or strong plastic) are often quite shallow in profile, whereas the softer examples need to use a steeper, more conical shape to maintain sufficient structural rigidity and hence extend the working frequency range.   However, even with a 'soft' dome, if the profile is too steep, the breakup mode may be sufficiently severe to produce a response peak up to 4 dB high.

Heavy well damped domes may have a surprisingly restricted response, and one well known example which is widely employed in European designs possesses a gently falling characteristic above 3.5 kHz.   Others, by fortuitous use of choice of profile and material, may be extended by a further two octaves to approximately 10 kHz.

There is nevertheless one appealing characteristic possessed by good mid-range dome units. Their subjective sound may be entirely free of the particular 'edgy' hardness exhibited to some degree by most cone units when operating in the mid-range, and in this respect, domes bear comparison to the film-type transducers such as the electrostatic. This largely accounts for the determined efforts on the part of many manufacturers to incorporate such units into their system designs.

Cones (MF)

A coned driver, if of moderate size, may be designed to cover the entire LF/MF range to a high standard. Such a unit may also prove a good choice for mid-range use only. A number of recent three way high performance systems have utilised mid-range drivers which are also capable of bass reproduction in suitable enclosures. By definition, these units have a wide bandwidth, this being advantageous when selecting the optimum crossover point. Coned LF/MF drivers ranging in size from 100 mm to 200 mm have been used, with a separate sub-enclosure to isolate the driver from the back air pressure generated by the LF unit. Specialised mid-units tend to be on the small side (typically 80 mm piston radius) since this provides sufficient output down to 250 Hz or so and yet presents a small enough source for satisfactory dispersion at the high frequency end of the range. Models may be fitted with an integral enclosure or more simply, supplied with a sealed chassis back, the space behind the diaphragm fitted with suitable acoustic absorbent. A typical response curve can be uniform from 250 Hz to 6 kHz.

The theory which concerns controlled smooth transitions from one vibrational mode to another is especially relevant in the case of mid-range diaphragms, since they generally operate in piston mode in the lower range and in controlled breakup in the upper band, with the broad region dividing the two generally appearing between 1 and 2 kHz. It is thus essential that the diaphragm be well terminated at its boundaries, and that the shape and choice of material be conductive to good transient behaviour, free of significant delayed resonance. Shallow flared profiles have given quite good results especially in thermoplastic cones.

A new material is being used by the British Company of Bowers and Wilkins in the production of a mid-range unit that incorporates many of the above design principles. The cone is a fairly rigid structure formed from an open weave nylon fibre (polyamide) coated with the usual viscous-elastic PVA damping layer, which also serves to stiffen the structure.

There is a final point worthy of consideration when choosing a cone material. In a practical driver there is often some maximum sound pressure level above which audible quality deterioration occurs. This effect cannot be ascribed to the magnet, suspension or crossover non-linearity and is believed to result from a gross compression at the neck of the cone due to the applied force exceeding the elastic limit of the material. Operation in such regions means that the material fails to return to its original dimensions for some time (ranging from milliseconds to hours), and the resulting distortion, being of the hysteresis type, is particularly unpleasant.

It appears that some plastics of apparently suitable acoustic properties for cone manufacture suffer from this effect more than others, and it may well be an important consideration if high sound pressure levels are required. The new polypropylene cone material is particularly good in this respect.

Suspensions (MF)

The suspension is usually integral with the diaphragm in dome units, a doped, half-roll surround being formed at the perimeter.

Rocking is one unwanted mode of vibration which may be troublesome with single suspension designs. Soft dome assemblies are noted for this defect which results in subharmonics and increased intermodulation distortion. The mass of the assembly plus the shape and physical constraints of the surround are critical factors here. One obvious solution is the adoption of a double suspension. However, even two moderately spaced suspensions take up considerable depth and necessitate a long motor-coil former, which may be disadvantageous in a dome radiator. The resulting assembly is difficult to produce and is generally restricted to the more expensive designs such as the West German unit illustrated in Fig.5.7.

Another solution could be to employ ferro-fluid in the magnet gap, this providing a strong centring contribution and suppressing the rocking mode.

In the case of cone diaphragms, the suspensions are usually manufactured from conventional corrugated fabric, but due regard must be paid to the possibility of any self-resonance which may be audible in the mid-range.

Surround (MF)

The choice of a surround material presents a considerable problem for a designer of a unit covering mid and higher frequencies. The commonly used materials — neoprene, p.v.c. etc. — have mechanical properties which vary greatly with frequency. Ideally, the energy absorption property should be resistive and constant, but invariably the elastic rubber-type materials are hysteretic, and show a memory effect, i.e. a time lag exists between deformation and subsequent recovery. Consequently with increasing frequency, these materials stiffen and become less absorptive. To date a lightly impregnated grade of foam plastic has proved most successful at the higher frequencies.

Since little excursion is required of a mid-range unit the surround

(a)

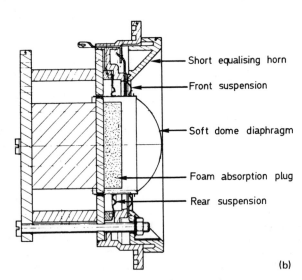

Short equalising horn

Front suspension

Soft dome diaphragm

Foam absorption plug

Rear suspension

(b)

Figure 5.7 (a) *50 mm diameter double-suspension, fabric dome mid-unit.* (b) *Cross-section of (a). (Courtesy SEL/ITT).*

profile may be a simple flat strip, no half-roll or other device being strictly necessary.

Motor systems (MF)

The magnet structures of cone and dome mid units present a great contrast in terms of their size; whereas a scaled down assembly of typically 19 mm diameter is sufficient for the former, the dome requires a massive structure energising a 50 mm, or even larger pole.

Ideally the magnet diameter for a mid-range cone should be small, so that the minimum reflecting surface is present immediately behind the cone. This suggests the use of an alnico or columnar magnet rather than the ceramic 'pancake' type. Too many mid-units have inadequate acoustic clearance behind the diaphragm, and the resulting colourations are clearly audible.

In an effort to lower the fundamental resonance of dome designs, the pole is often centre bored; ideally this assumes a tapered form to reduce pipe standing waves, with the aperture often leading to a sealed rear chamber filled with absorptive material.

The use of ferro-fluid may prove advantageous where the short term power input is high and the cone excursion small. Large increases in power handling are possible with its use; up to two or three times in the short term (for example, 1.5 minutes).

Where very low distortion levels are required, secondary harmonic sources such as eddy currents in the poles must be eliminated. Suitable remedies include copper plating, lamination of the pole structures or the use of a high resistivity magnetic alloy for the poles themselves. Again the use of ferro-fluid may offer some reduction in distortion.

The necessity for predictable and controlled breakup modes in mid-range diaphragm assemblies means that the location and method of attaching the lead out wires to the motor coil must be carefully considered. Ideally the exits should be symmetrical, preferably at the motor coil former rather than haphazardly stuck to the cone as is frequently the case. The latter method promotes asymmetrical break-up and high rocking modes, especially at the higher frequencies.

5.5 HIGH-FREQUENCY UNITS

The general classification for HF units embraces a 1 kHz to 30 kHz range, overlapping by an octave or so the upper mid band. The total range covers five octaves, which is virtually impossible for a single unit to achieve satisfactorily, and hence the classification is loosely split into low range (1 kHz—10 kHz); full range (3 kHz—18 kHz) and high range or super treble (8 kHz—30 kHz).

Conventional cone diaphragms are rarely used for this frequency band in high performance systems as this range operates a cone in the

Figure 5.8   25 mm 'soft-dome' HF unit (courtesy Son Audax)

higher breakup region where the output is falling and is generally both
irregular and unpredictable.

Dome diaphragms (HF)

Domes are undoubtedly the most common form of HF diaphragm and
are available in a wide variety of shape, size and material. Additionally,
the chassis and front plate structure may be acoustically tailored to
provide equalisation of both polar and/or axial response characteristics.

The 25 mm soft fabric dome first became popular in Europe and its
use has since spread throughout the world, with more than thirty types
now available from various manufacturers (Fig.5.8). (Soft dome HF
units are also produced in the 34 mm and 19 mm sizes).

Plastics are also used for the production of dome units, notably
melinex, often in a laminated form bonded to a p.v.c. damping layer.
9 mm, 25 mm and 38 mm sizes are all available with fundamental resonant frequencies ranging from 600 Hz to 2 kHz, and upper cutoff frequencies from 25 kHz down to 15 kHz.

Yamaha have produced a beryllium HF unit of 30 mm nominal
diameter, whose first breakup mode is beyond 30 kHz, ensuring virtual
piston operation over the entire 2 kHz to 18 kHz useable band. The
diaphragm thickness is 30 μ with a mass of 30 mg which compares with
a soft dome counterpart at 100 mg and similar thickness. The rigidity
of beryllium is too high to employ an integral suspension and instead
a separate, tangentially pleated cloth surround is used, with a damping
coating composed of two resins to dissipate energy at the rim. Some

TABLE 5.2

	Density (ρ) (kg/m^3)	Young's modulus (E) (N/m^2 × 10^{10})	Specific modulus (E/ρ) (m/s × 10^7)
Aluminium	2.7	6.1	2.3
Titanium	4.5	11.6	2.6
Iron	7.9	20	2.5
Magnesium	1.8	4.5	2.6
Beryllium	1.8	25.0	14.0
Boron	2.4	39.0	16.5

rigidity figures are shown in Table 5.2.

While a fabric dome often possesses a quite well damped fundamental resonance due to the applied tacky compound, the plastic domes may show quite a high Q, as much as 10 at resonance. Various means may be used to control the Q ranging from applied damping to acoustic anti-resonant circuits formed by venting the rear cavity behind the dome into various resistively damped chambers present in the magnet structure

In the upper range above 8 kHz or so, the plastic domes may suffer from breakup problems, either due to lack of rigidity or resonances in the surround. One example possesses a surround resonance near 10 kHz, which causes a marked rise in second harmonic distortion. This may be cured by appropriate damping on the inside of the suspension. Where the dome itself is in resonance a doping layer can be applied to the centre or alternatively a small plug of polyurethane foam placed in contact with the offending area. Other techniques include the juxtaposition of a so-called phase correction plate which may block, direct or delay the output. This works over limited frequency bands, controlling the radiation from specific areas of the dome to smooth the integrated far-field response.

An unusual and highly successful example of a hard dome HF unit is undoubtedly the HF1300 family, manufactured by Celestion, (UK) (Fig.5.9). Variations of this design have been in production since the mid 1950s, and are still used in a number of systems. Almost all of the details of its construction have proved to be critical, these range from the particular grade of cured phenolic impregnated fabric used for the diaphragm, to the spacing of the phase correction plate. The centre dome is conical, about 19 mm in diameter, and has a shallow, rather broad surround actually larger in area than the dome itself. The unit as a whole has an overall diameter of 38 mm. The surround is in fact the main radiating element; piston operation holds to beyond 10 kHz and the diaphragm is particularly free of hysteresis effects. This, in conjunction with its relatively uniform axial frequency response, accounts for its unusually favourable subjective qualities.

Figure 5.9   Rigid phenolic doped fabric dome HF unit, with sophisticated acoustic loading. (Front cavity resonator, rear energy-coupled resonator, diaphragm damping

The diaphragm's intrinsic pressure characteristic shows a peak at fundamental resonance (1.7 kHz) which is damped by resistively controlled air vents to the cavity within the enclosed pot magnet. The centre pole has a conical profile to closely follow the contour of the underside of the dome, this placing the first rear standing wave mode at a very high frequency. The output of the naked diaphragm falls above 7 kHz or so, and to correct this a perforated front plate is fitted, formed so as to follow a similar contour to that of the diaphragm. This results in a damped resonant cavity loading the diaphragm, and also provides a delay path between the dome and surround radiation. The output is thus uniformly maintained on axis to 14 kHz. Good examples may demonstrate a ±2 dB characteristic from 2 kHz to 14 kHz, with the range 4 kHz to 12 kHz held within ±1 dB limits.

A super treble unit is usually employed with the HF1300 to extend the response over the final half octave, although its use is not strictly necessary in view of the minimal programme content above 15 kHz from disc and broadcast transmissions.

Motor systems (HF)

With suitable coil winding techniques, the larger treble units with 30 mm centre poles and over will have power ratings of 8—15 W corresponding to a system rating of the order of 100 W on continuous programme. The smaller 19 mm motor coils may have ratings below 8 W, and these are often provided with fuse protection in the accompanying speaker system to guard against high level, high frequency drive which may occur during tape spooling or amplifier instability.

As has been mentioned in connection with the other drivers, the application of ferro-fluid to the magnet gap will offer considerable protection against thermal overload, and a viscosity grade may be chosen which will also provide damping of the fundamental resonance and control of rocking, the latter proving a problem with HF as well as MF dome units. At the design stage the significant variation in ferrofluid viscosity with gap temperature, often up to 40°C, must be considered if such damping forms part of a crossover analysis.

When high acoustic levels are required of dome mid and LF units their relatively low efficiency necessitates very large magnets and these can prove costly as a result. Where a moderate quality deterioration is tolerable, horn loaded treble or mid domes are employed. The horn offers control of directivity and gives a better acoustic match between the air load and the diaphragm. Using phenolic or aluminium domes with horn loading, efficiencies of up to 20% are possible, contrasting with the 1 to 2% typical of simple direct radiator dome units.

5.6 FULL-RANGE UNITS

A few examples of full-range moving-coil drivers are in manufacture, and although at present they do not completely satisfy the 'high performance' criteria, certain of the techniques involved are worthy of note.

Full-range cone driver

Jordan designed an interesting example of an aluminium cone unit which was first produced in the mid 1960s. The diaphragm possesses a hyperbolic flare with a centre dome stiffener and a matched, viscous treated plastic foam surround. The cone diameter is 100 mm which was considered to be an optimum compromise between LF radiating area (the unit was intended for use in domestic applications) and adequate dispersion at the higher frequencies. It certainly achieved most of the designer's aims and although not produced in very large quantities was undoubtedly a commercial success. It demonstrated at a fairly early stage the value of a flared cone profile and good termination, plus the effectiveness of a high linearity magnet system and non-resonant chassis.

In West Germany (JWM Systems) development is currently proceeding on the design of another full range driver. This employs a flexible diaphragm engineered so that the mechanical load presented to the motor coil is almost wholly resistive and independent of frequency. The moving structure consists of a pre-loaded flat web of synthetic fibre (polyamide/nylon group) impregnated with an air drying visco-elastic coating, probably of the PVA type.

A split motor coil, using differential drive is employed, with the injection of an offset current to allow centring of the coil in the magnet gap. A star-shaped plastic foam section acts as a supporting and stiffening component. With a fundamental resonance partly dependent on the drive amplitude (20—40 Hz), the unit is nominally flat to 6 kHz, above with a 6 dB/octave boost equalisation is required. The maximum displacement was quoted at 3 mm and the sensitivity as 3.2 W for 96 dB s.p.l. at 1 m. At low frequencies the full diaphragm area moves, but with increasing frequency the radiating area contracts smoothly with resistive control toward the centre, resulting in the small source required for good high-range performance[6].

REFERENCES

1. Harwood, H. D., 'New B.B.C. monitoring loudspeaker', *Wireless World,* March, April and May (1968)
2. Harwood, H. D., 'Loudspeaker distortion associated with LF signals', *J. Audio Engng. Soc.* 20, No.9 (1972)
3. King, J., 'Loudspeaker voice coils', *J. Audio Engng. Soc.*, 18, No.1, 34—43 (1970)
4. Ferrofluidics Corporation, Massachusetts, USA, Leaflet, *Ferrofluidics*
5. Yuasa, Y. and Greenberg, S., 'The beryllium dome diaphragm', *Proc. Audio Engrs. Soc. 52nd Convention,* October—November (1975)
6. Pfau, E., 'Ein Nuer Dynamischer Lautsprecher mit extrem nachgeibiger Membran', *Funkshau,* March (1974)

BIBLIOGRAPHY

Beranek, L., *Acoustics,* McGraw-Hill, London (1954)

Briggs, G. A., *More About Loudspeakers,* Wharfedale Wireless Works, Idle, Yorkshire (1963)

Cohen, A. B., *Hi Fi Loudspeakers and Enclosures,* Newnes-Butterworth London (1975)

Gilliom, J. R., Boliver, P. and Boliver, L., 'Design problems of high level cone loudspeakers', *J. Audio Engng Soc.*, 25, No.5 (1977)

Ishiwatari, K., Sakamoto, N., Kawabata, H., Takeuchi, H. and Shimuzu, T., 'Use of boron for H.F. dome loudspeakers', *J. Audio Engng Soc.*, 26, No.4 (1978)

Jordan, E. J., *Loudspeakers,* London (1963)

KEF Electronics Ltd., *You and Your Loudspeaker,* KEF Electronics Ltd., (c. 1970)

National Panasonic, *The Technics SB1000 High Linearity Loudspeaker,* Technics Promotional Leaflet

6

Systems and crossovers

Previous chapters have shown that a single diaphragm driver cannot meet the standard implied by the phrase 'high performance'. Unfortunately, the need for a large area to give effective low frequency reproduction conflicts with the very small diaphragm necessary for satisfactory HF performance. In consequence, the high performance loudspeaker is invariably a 'system' which in its simplest form consists of an enclosure of defined acoustic properties plus two or more specialised drivers and an electrical filter. The latter directs the correct frequency range into the appropriate drivers and is termed the crossover network (Fig.6.1). In advanced systems it may also be responsible for other functions such as attenuation and equalisation.

Certain benefits result from this division of the working frequency range. All modulation distortions are considerably reduced, particularly FM*, the latter produced by the physical movement of a low frequency diaphragm whilst simultaneously reproducing a higher frequency. Some residual FM, will remain in all systems except for those special cases where bass horns or considerably spaced drivers are employed, as the low frequency unit will still occupy a proportion of the enclosure surface. Some energy from the higher frequency units will be incident on the LF diaphragm and will undergo modulating excursion as a result or, viewed differently, a proportion of the acoustic load on the higher frequency drivers will be modulated by the LF diaphragm movement.

With appropriate choice of matching drivers, and their working frequency range, acceptably close control of directivity may also be achieved. The accompanying uniformity of off-axis response improves stereo imaging and contributes to a neutral reverberant sound field in the listening room. The presence of discontinuities in an off-axis response may often be heard in a resulting colouration of the reverberant sound field.

Skilful crossover design will result in good integration between the outputs of adjacent drivers to ensure a uniform frontal output through the crossover frequencies. The optimum listening axis may be adjusted to that pertaining under actual conditions of use, as this may differ from the standard axial test positions (Fig.6.2).

* Frequency modulation or Doppler distortion

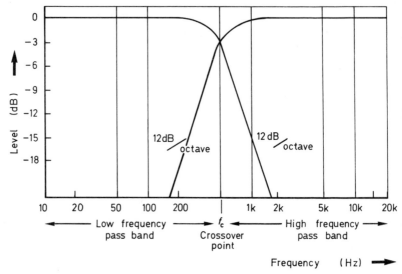

Figure 6.1   Two-way crossover filter response (2nd order 12 dB/octave). (High frequency power fed to HF unit, low frequency power fed to LF unit.)

With a loudspeaker designed for stereo use, the directivity in the vertical plane can be fairly narrow, as the relative heights of speaker and subject fall within reasonable limits. A suggested standard for vertical directivity might be 'the deviation from the axial response shall be less than 3 dB over a ±15° vertical angle, up to 12 kHz'.

In the horizontal plane, a dispersion angle of twice this figure is desirable. While some designers aim for maximum dispersion at all frequencies, there is no real evidence that the stereo image quality improves as a result. Harwood suggests on the evidence of BBC tests that there may be an optimum directivity for stereo. A very small, wide dispersion BBC speaker gave poorer imaging results than a much larger model which was consistently closer to a ±30° directivity standard[1]. With wide dispersion designs the reverberant sound intensity will be higher relative to the direct sound than with narrower types, and perhaps this may partially account for the degraded imaging.

The need for a uniform, symmetrical directivity in the horizontal plane dictates that the main drivers be mounted in a vertical-in-line formation. There is no doubt that this particular configuration is important to stereo image stability, and if further evidence were needed, data collected during a recent consumer test of thirty pairs of loudspeakers provided indications that vertical inline systems (Fig.6.3) gave superior stereo results[2]. (See also section on Phase, p.199.)

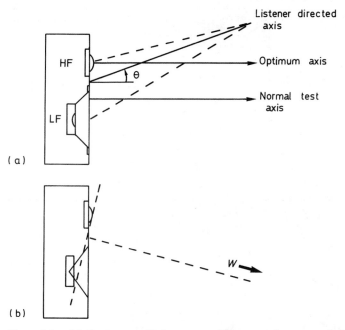

Figure 6.2 (a) Optimum radiation axes. (Crossover phase control produces listener directed axis at angle θ to normal axis.) (b) Combined in-phase wave front, W, directed off-axis by mounting method. Advancement of LF driver radiation centre to plane of HF driver will allow correction of inter-unit time delay/ phase shift on axis.

6.1 SYSTEM DESIGN

There are no hard and fast rules for the design of a successful system. Two distinct classes exist; those systems designed in every detail by a loudspeaker manufacturer who makes his own drive units, and the systems assembled from o.e.m. (original equipment manufacturer) drivers from outside sources. In the case of the former, the engineer has complete control of the design process and can produce a system more or less precisely to meet a given standard of performance.

From the desired specification he may establish the optimum driver and enclosure characteristics, design the units to meet these requirements and thus complete the system with the addition of a matching enclosure and crossover.

More often than not, even the manufacturer who makes his own drivers will not have the resources to design individual units for each

Figure 6.2 (c) A three-way system with time aligned drivers, 24 dB/octave, crossover (acoustic) and low diffraction enclosure forms (Courtesy KEF Electronics)

system. For economic reasons he is forced to rationalise and is likely to produce a fairly well ordered range of drivers each capable, (with possibly some small detail variation), of meeting the needs of several systems.

The perfect driver has yet to be developed, and each presents its own unique engineering and performance compromise. While the independent designer has a vast number of permutations and combinations to choose from, he has little control over driver uniformity and the very

Figure 6.3   A four-way vertical-in-line system (18 dB/octave electrical crossover with controlled listening axis) (BC3, Courtesy of Spendor Ltd.)

existence of such a wide selection brings with it its own special problems.

A high performance system is by definition a consistent product, and it is therefore vital that the driver characteristics remain constant during production.   The possibility of any significant variation must be investigated at the design stage, a 'centre' specification should be established with allowable deviation limits, and provision made to correct the inevitable remaining tolerances, for example in the system crossover.

The variations themselves may concern any aspect of performance but once a unit is chosen and its manufacture kept under close control, the criteria of frequency response and sensitivity alone are usually sufficient to completely quantify the unit for production.

Factors affecting the choice of drive units

Many system engineers rely on intuition when selecting a driver line up. Familiarity with a large number of units is a prerequisite, and the choice is generally made on the basis of the limitations of performance discussed in Chapter 5, but occasionally there are exceptions.

For example the better class of 200 mm plastic cone driver currently manufactured in the UK can produce a good performance that extends to 5 kHz, well beyond that which is attainable using normal paper-pulp cones. This allows the crossover point to be placed between 3—4 kHz, high enough to consider transfer to a small 25 or 19 mm high frequency dome unit for the upper range. Some excellent systems of necessarily limited maximum acoustic output have been produced along these lines from KEF Electronics (R103, R104 etc.), Spendor Audio Systems, (BC1, BC2) and Bowers and Wilkins, (DM4, DM2).

Cone theory indicates that such a 200 mm driver will be operating in breakup above 600 Hz or so and this is indeed often the case. However, the particularly consistent properties of the synthetic cone material employed allow the designer to adequately control the breakup modes such that the range may be smoothly extended by a further three octaves. A normal paper-pulp cone cannot usually achieve this level of performance and in consequence the crossover point for a high performance application would need to be placed at around 1 kHz. This would entail the use of an additional mid-range driver to meet the bass unit at 1 kHz, and a further HF unit would probably be required to complete the frequency range.

High performance systems

The need for adequate acoustic output from a true high performance system virtually dictates that the minimum size of bass unit should be 250 or 300 mm in diameter; (the 200 mm based systems are generally insufficiently loud for professional monitoring).

Low frequency drivers

The choice of LF driver will depend on the level of colouration tolerable together with considerations of bandwidth (LF excursion), efficiency, power handling and enclosure size.

Depending on the volume of the enclosure, the LF unit may be loaded in several ways, the electro-acoustic properties of the individual driver being an important factor in this context. In domestic locations compact systems are strongly favoured for aesthetic reasons, and in general, no loudspeaker system should be larger than is strictly necessary.

Few LF drivers will function adequately beyond 1 kHz and the maximum safe crossover frequency is generally 500 to 700 Hz for the better 250 mm units and 350 to 500 Hz for the 300 mm sizes. With these larger drivers a further reduction to 250 Hz may help to reduce subjective colouration particularly as regards voice reproduction.

Mid frequency drivers

Taking 350 Hz as the basic lower limit, it is desirable that the mid-range unit give an adequate performance from at least two octaves below, that is, 100 Hz. It almost goes without saying that its range should possess a reasonably uniform pressure response free of significant resonances or colourations. Such a driver is usually a cone unit 80 to 200 mm in diameter, often capable of bass/mid range coverage in its own right.

The better examples of mid-frequency driver will have a clean output up to 5 or 6 kHz allowing the transition to an HF unit to occur at 3 kHz; (ideally the upper range of the mid unit should extend further but this is rarely achieved).

To date, the dome mid-range units that have been produced range in diameter from 35 to 85 mm, and considerable problems have been experienced in the attempt to provide a sufficiently wide response. To cover the basic 350 Hz to 5 kHz mid band, an overall 100 Hz to 15 kHz response is desirable, amounting to seven octaves. The best examples so far cope reasonably well from 350 Hz to 5 kHz, but necessitate crossover points around 600 Hz and 4 kHz with accompanying high slopes of perhaps third order, 18 dB/octave roll-off.

High frequency drivers

Sensitivity will be an important factor in the selection of a HF driver since few high quality designs are efficient. Some recent examples of 25 mm dome units have managed to combine qualities of smoothness, high linearity and adequate sensitivity and these are now widely employed since at this quality level, cone units are virtually ruled out. If higher levels of acoustic output are required, this may only be obtained via horn loading.

With a crossover point probably in the range 3 kHz to 6 kHz, the HF unit should ideally have a response extension below 1 kHz for optimum crossover performance. Most 25 mm dome units fulfill this condition, although the magnitude of the Q at fundamental resonance must be taken into consideration.

The broad overlap of driver response is best shown in terms of a system, Fig.6.4, illustrating the responses of an ideal 'three-way' set of drivers.

Sensitivity matching

Ideally the in-band working sensitivities of the drivers making up a

(Note considerable overlap ideally required)

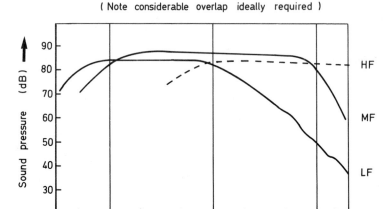

Figure 6.4   Ideal driver responses for three-way system (f_c at 500 Hz and 4 kHz)

system should be equal when measured on the system axis. This should hold true after all the equalisation, compensation and crossover loss taken has been included.

The latter effect can be difficult to predict and it is best to initially establish the low frequency sensitivity. The mid and treble drivers should be selected so that sufficient sensitivity remains in hand. Since even high quality drivers can vary in sensitivity by up to ±1.5 dB in production, often some selection or final balance adjustment will be required for the completed system. Moderate resistive attenuation does not unduly affect the mid and high frequency driver and crossover performance, but is likely to significantly disturb an LF unit especially near the bass resonance, and sensitivity control must be ruled out for the bass unless an auto transformer is employed.

It is therefore usual to direct couple the LF unit via the crossover, and to reserve any attenuation for the other drivers.

If the crossover is an active electronic design, separate power amplifiers feed each driver and sensitivity matching is easily accomplished via gain control. Nevertheless, the sensitivities and power handling must still be chosen with due regard to the maximum acoustic output of the system as a whole.

6.2 THE CROSSOVER NETWORK

Classically, a crossover network consists of a passive, high-power filter circuit designed using standard filter theory, commonly to a Butter-

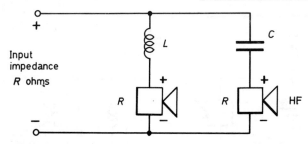

Figure 6.5   First order circuit and equations, $L = R/(2\pi f_C)$, $C = 1/(2\pi f_C R)$; *e.g.*
$R = 8\ \Omega$, $f_C = 3\ kHz$, $L = 0.42\ mH$ *and* $C = 6.6\ \mu F$ *(6 dB/octave rolloff)*

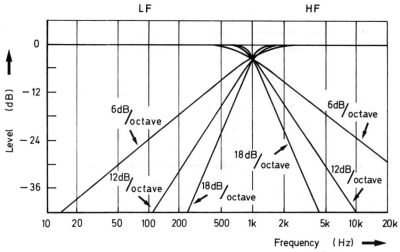

Figure 6.6   Two-way crossover responses (6, 12 and 18 dB/octave rolloffs)

worth response characteristic which provides maximum response flatness with a reasonably well defined roll-off.

The simplest form of crossover is a two-way network of first order which consists of a single inductor to direct bass power to the low frequency unit and a single capacitor, which passes treble power to the high frequency unit.   Such networks are inexpensive and are often found in low-priced systems (Figs.6.5 and 6.6).

However this form is quite inadequate for high performance applications, except in those exceptional cases where extremely wide range drivers of defined spacing (including a common radiation plane) and dispersion are employed.   In the latter case, it provides the most accurate method of achieving minimum phase shift between the drivers and

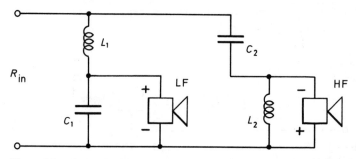

Figure 6.7   2nd order crossover circuits and equations: $L_1 = R_{in}/(2\sqrt{2}\pi f_c)$, $L_2 = R_{in}/(\sqrt{2}\pi f_c)$, $C_1 = 1/(\sqrt{2}\pi f_c R_{in})$, $C_2 = 1/(2\sqrt{2}\pi f_c R_{in})$ *(12 dB/octave)*

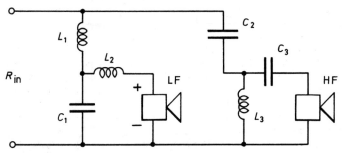

Figure 6.8   3rd order crossover circuit and equations (see Table 6.1).
$L_1 = 3L_2 = L_3/2 = 3R_{in}/(4\pi f_c)$
$C_1 = 2C_2 = 2C_3/3 = 2/(3\pi f_c R_{in})$ *(18 dB/octave)*

hence allows the 'minimum phase' or less accurately 'linear phase' class of speakers to be designed. However such systems with displaced drivers, will inevitably suffer from poor vertical response due to the broad driver overlap and the resulting interference patterns.

Higher order networks

To provide adequate control of the vertical dispersion in vertical in-line driver arrangements, the region of overlap between the respective operating ranges must be narrow. Higher order networks are virtually essential with good results achieved by using a third order 18 dB/octave rolloff type in the Butterworth configuration. A second order, 12 dB/octave circuit is shown in Fig.6.7.

While second order networks are often used as a compromise, there is considerable advantage to be gained by using the third order. The

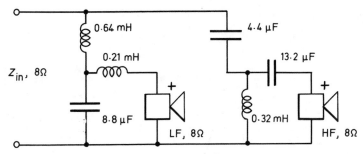

Figure 6.9 Theoretical 8 Ω, 3 kHz, 3rd order crossover circuit (based on equations in caption to Fig.6.8)

equations for the latter are given in Fig.6.8 and a numerical example in Fig.6.9.

The total pressure response of a system is flatter with 3rd order than with 2nd order and is in fact virtually identical to the first order in this respect. The fifth order also has this property but is probably not worth pursuing on grounds of cost and circuit loss, except where an active is involved. Additionally the phase response of the third order is more favourable through the crossover region. The outputs of a second order network are in anti-phase at the crossover point, a condition corrected by reversing the leads to the treble driver but resulting in a total displacement elsewhere. The odd order networks by contrast give a 90° shift.

In addition to the tighter control of the working bands provided by the third order 18 dB/octave configuration, this type may also be readily modified to include equalisation tailoring sections, either as additions to the basic network or by alteration of existing arms; for example, by the inclusion of resistive damping across inductors or capacitors. Fourth order networks are also used, notable in the 'delay compensated' designs, since the phase shift at crossover is zero, and the driver output interaction minimal. (See Appendix 3.)

Mistermination

In practice, crossover networks may be further complicated by matching problems. The constant crossover input resistance offered by Butterworth crossover theory assumes the input of the impedance drivers also to be a constant resistance, nominally 8 Ω for the network illustrated in Fig.6.9.

Section 2.3, Region C, shows that at only one part of the frequency range is the terminal impedance of a moving coil driver a fairly constant resistance. Figure 6.10 shows that at lower frequencies a more or less well damped fundamental resonance occurs with the motional impe-

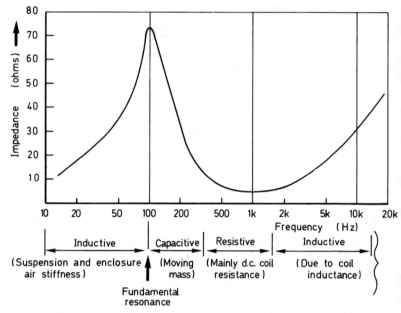

Figure 6.10   Moving coil driver input impedance

dance passing through the inductive, resistive and capacitive regions[3].

At higher frequencies the inductance of the motor coil becomes significant producing a rise in impedance. When such a complex load is connected to a standard filter, mis-termination occurs, with resulting irregularities in both the amplitude and phase response of the filter.

An active crossover is essentially immune to these problems, since perfect filter network termination is provided in the circuitry, with power amplifiers voltage-driving the motor coil in an ideal fashion. The advantages of this approach are discussed more fully in Section 6.3 on active crossovers.

Figure 6.9 is a theoretical realisation of a two-way 8 Ω network operating nominally at 3.0 kHz. The network from a successful commercial system is reproduced in Fig.6.11. As it is difficult to see any resemblance between these two, how then may crossovers be designed if the basic theory appears to have so little relevance? The answer lies in an extension of the filter network theory to include the other relevant factors present in the total system. This involves viewing the crossover response in terms of the combined acoustic output of the drivers instead of theoretical voltages on the driver terminals. By moving outside and in front of the enclosure it becomes obvious that the crossover requirement is for the overall response to be in terms of the acoustic

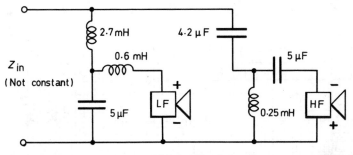

Figure 6.11 Successful commercial 3 kHz, 3rd order crossover (KEF R104 system)

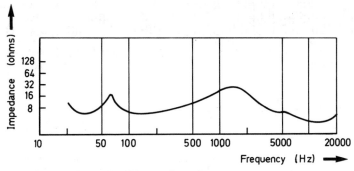

Figure 6.12 KEF Model 104, impedance frequency

output of the drivers. Hence the driver parameters — motor coil inductance and resistance, frequency and phase response and the motional impedance near resonance — must be accounted for in the network theory while ensuring that the system as a whole still offers a sensible load for the matching amplifier. The characteristic loading generated in Fig.6.11 is shown in the system impedance curve, Fig.6.12, and is clearly not a constant 8 Ω.

The lack of correspondence between the measured acoustic output and the calculated crossover filter response is shown in Fig.6.13. The first-generation network of Fig.6.11 was further developed to incorporate compensation for both the motional impedance variation due to the fundamental resonance, and the intrinsic motor and coil characteristic of the HF unit. The equivalent circuit for these components was included in a computer programme together with information concerning its amplitude response, and a new network was synthesised, which was

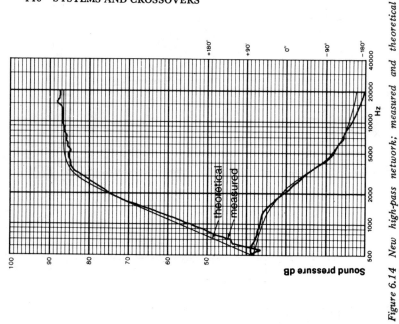

Figure 6.13 HF unit output; measured and theoretical responses (courtesy KEF Electronics). Circuit of Figure 6.11

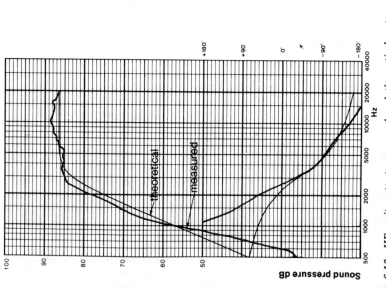

Figure 6.14 New high-pass network; measured and theoretical responses (courtesy KEF Electronics). Circuit of Figure 6.13

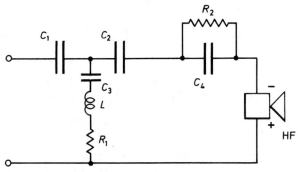

Figure 6.15   Theoretical circuit of new 3rd order compensated high-pass section (courtesy KEF Electronics)

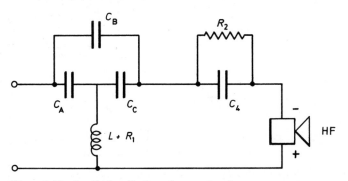

Figure 6.16   Practical realisation of new network;

$$C_A = \frac{C_1 C_2}{C_1 + C_2 + C_3}, \qquad C_B = \frac{C_1 C_3}{C_1 + C_2 + C_3}, \qquad C_C = \frac{C_2 C_3}{C_1 + C_2 + C_3}$$

designed to give the intended 18 dB/octave Butterworth response in the driver's acoustic output.

The success of the new network is shown in the close agreement between the measured and calculated responses shown in Fig.6.14. Figure 6.15 illustrates the theoretical form of this new compensated high-pass network with Fig.6.16 illustrating a practical realisation, and Fig.6.17 carrying the numerical values used in commercial system.

Figure 6.16 was derived by applying the Star-Delta transform to Fig. 6.15. It is sufficient to view the circuit as a lumped approximation and it can be readily seen that the controlled Q of the shunt indicator provides a first slope of 6 dB/octave this summing with the driver's natural 12 dB/octave slope.

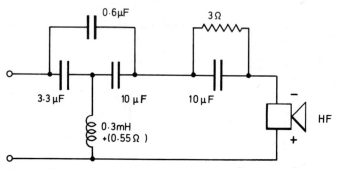

Figure 6.17 Values used in commercial system KEF R104AB (courtesy KEF Electronics)

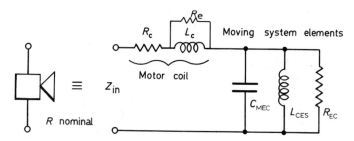

Figure 6.18 Moving-coil driver equivalent circuit (R_e are eddy losses)

The second capacitor, C_4, is equivalent to the moving mass of the diaphragm and is part of the complete synthesis. C_4 causes the derivative of the current waveform in the driver to follow the Butterworth curve, this resulting in constant motor coil acceleration. Interestingly the values of the basic 'T' section network are quite close to those established theoretically for a perfect driver.

Driver impedance compensation

A moving coil driver may be represented by an electrical equivalent circuit consisting of the coil components R_c and L_c and the transformed mechanical components, L_{CES}, C_{MEC} and R_{EC} (see Fig.6.18).

With an LF unit the fundamental resonance is deliberately exploited and does not require compensation in this context. However, with mid

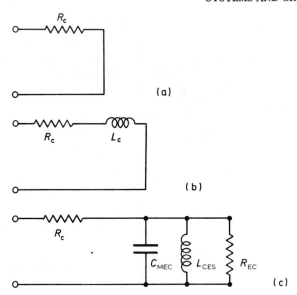

Figure 6.19 Simplified forms over specific frequency bands (from Fig.6.18). (a) At mid frequencies, (b) at high frequencies and (c) at near resonance; low frequencies

and HF drivers the fundamental resonance can be sufficiently near the crossover region to cause mis-termination and is worth neutralising. Figure 6.18 can be simplified if specific frequency ranges are separately considered (Fig.6.19).

The consequences of crossover filter mis-termination are clearly shown in Fig.6.20. A crossover at 7 kHz consisting of a single capacitor was to be used with an HF unit having the response curve 'A'. While the rolloff in the resulting curve 'B' approximates to the desired 6 dB/octave slope down to 3.5 kHz, the increase in motional impedance at resonance (850 Hz) causes the output to rise sharply, almost peaking to the driver output level in the absence of the crossover. Below resonance the slope now follows an 18 dB/octave rolloff due to the addition of the intrinsic driver rolloff. At the highest frequencies the crossover capacitor begins to weakly resonate with the motor coil inductance, producing a rise in output above 10 kHz. The overall curve bears little resemblance to the required smooth transition with 6 dB/octave slope.

The motor coil inductance may largely be compensated by a series R and C combination connected in parallel with the driver terminals (Fig.6.21). If the coil values are R_c and L_c the equalisation components

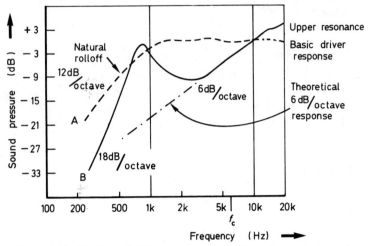

Figure 6.20 Moving-coil driver response; A: alone, B: with 1st order series capacitor, f_c = 7 kHz

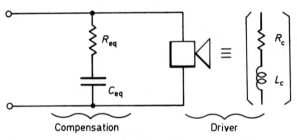

Figure 6.21 Circuit and equations for motor-coil inductance operation; R_{eq} = R_c, C_{eq} = L_c/R_c^2

to a first approximation are as follows:

$$R_{eq} = R_c$$

and

$$C_{eq} = \frac{L_c}{R_c^2}$$

A typical 25 mm diameter motor coil for an HF unit might have a 6.4 Ω

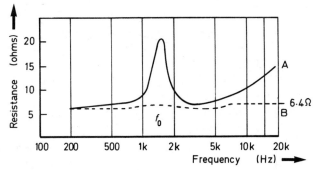

Figure 6.22   Curve A: impedance curve of 19 mm plastic dome HF unit. Curve B: as for Curve A but with compensation circuit of Fig.6.23

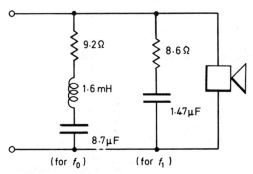

Figure 6.23   Compensation circuit for non-uniform impedance of HF driver in Fig.6.22 (values determined by experiment)

resistance and a 0.15 mH inductance, giving respective values for R_{eq} and C_{eq} of 6.4 ohms and 0.366 μF.   The fact that this compensation is possible gives the designer some freedom in adjusting the response at extreme frequencies should the driver appear to need this.

Since the driver impedance rises at resonance, a simple compensation would consist of a series resonant circuit connected in parallel with the terminals, this largely accounting for the electrical equivalent components of the mechanical fundamental resonance, imparting a uniform impedance curve to the combination, the latter is shown before and after connection in Fig.6.22. The correction circuit used is shown in Fig.6.23.

The resonant frequency and its 'Q' may be determined from the impedance curve and an equalisation circuit synthesised to match this.

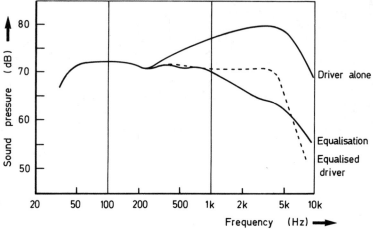

Figure 6.24   Equalisation of 200 mm plastic-cone driver

Alternatively the values may be found by experiment which in practice proves relatively simple to achieve.

Amplitude response equalisation

Equalisation of the driver impedance has been discussed, but to some degree this is rather academic unless the driver frequency response is already uniform, which is rarely the case. Thus in most high performance systems some form of response equalisation is almost invariably included.

Equalisation is only possible where the response irregularities are in the form of gentle trends rather than severe narrow band discontinuities with associated non-minimum phase characteristics. Clearly equalisation will also alter the input impedance of the entire system. A rise in impedance due to response correction is of little consequence, but a significant fall in input impedance as a result of compensation for response droop is undesirable due to amplifier matching problems. In practice, maximum sound pressure dips of around 2 dB may be equalised, and no limit appears necessary for the correction of driver response excesses, provided that they are gentle.

A typical 200 mm plastic cone bass/mid-range driver, when mounted in a 30—40 litre enclosure designed for stand mounting, will exhibit a well behaved axial response continuing to rise from approximately 400 Hz to 2 kHz and possibly beyond. If the criteria of a balanced and uniform axial sound pressure response is the objective, then equalisation must be applied. With active crossovers and equalisation stage may simply be added to the filter system, while in the case of the passive

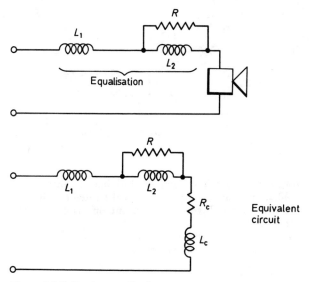

Figure 6.25 Passive equalisation

crossover filter, the equalisation is usually integrated with the crossover itself.

In the case of the 200 mm driver (Fig.6.24), the upwards response slope may be seen to approximate to 4 dB/octave, which characteristic could be compensated by a suitable series combination of inductance and resistance. When setting the values, the motor coil inductance must be taken into account, the latter typically of the order of 0.35 mH for a long-throw design. Approximately 2.2 mH of additional series inductance is required for the equalisation, and the inductor is split into 1.6 and 0.6 mH sections, the latter with a parallel 22 Ω resistor (Fig.6.25). The latter reduces the slope to match the rate of rise at the higher frequencies.

The third-order low-pass crossover 'T' configuration may be successfully combined with such equalisation by adding the necessary capacitor at the junction, and dimensioning it so that the desired turnover frequency is obtained (Fig.6.26). The Butterworth relation now of course no longer holds for the crossover and due note should be taken of the overall response of the filter/equaliser. With the configuration described, a peak may develop at the crossover point, which is usually adequately damped by an additional resistance, this fortunately is already present in the example given above (R in Fig.6.25).

When several such filter sections are cascaded, such as in the bandpass arm for a mid-range driver, further unwanted interaction may occur and hence adjustment of the calculated values is to be expected. A commercial four-way, 3rd order crossover is shown in Fig.6.27.

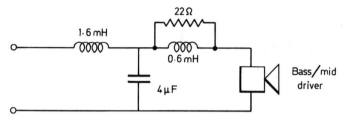

Figure 6.26   Equalised 3rd order low-pass filter incorporating Fig.6.25. $f_c \simeq 3\ kHz$, *18 dB/octave*

Crossover components

Modern high performance loudspeakers may need to handle considerable power of up to 200 W programme, equivalent to the rated continuous output of an amplifier when driven to clip point on programme of average energy distribution.

Clearly the crossover network should exhibit low losses, and possess an adequately high voltage and current capacity.

Cored inductors

In the case of an inductance in series with an LF unit, peak currents greater than 10A are possible.   With the sizeable inductance values required for third order 8 Ω networks at crossover frequencies in the 250 to 500 Hz range, it is very costly to produce air-cored components of sufficiently low loss, due to the winding resistance problems. Winding resistance may be exploited — to provide additional control of crossover filter Q or to reduce electromagnetic damping in an over-fluxed driver.

By incorporating a magnetic core the winding length may be considerably reduced but the core itself must not be allowed to enter saturation in service. Where ferrite cores are used, the ampere-turns rating is proportional to the core diameter for a given saturation point, the latter usually taken to be a 1% distortion level. If low distortion ratings for the system are important, (this particularly relevant in view of the odd rather than even harmonic nature of magnetic core distortion), then the core flux must be derated by as much as 50%.

If an inadequately rated inductor core is driven to saturation, the incremental inductance decreases. This is due to the failure of the core flux to continue to rise linearly with the increasing current through the component. Such a loss of dynamic inductance may produce a sudden reduction in the system impedance, particularly in low pass sections. This is likely to induce premature overload in the driving amplifier and consequently increased distortion. The overall result is a characteristic 'cracking' sound often incorrectly attributed to the amplifier.

In 100 W systems, ferrite cores of 19 mm diameter are adequate for inductors up to 5 mH, while at lower power levels, e.g. up to 50 W,

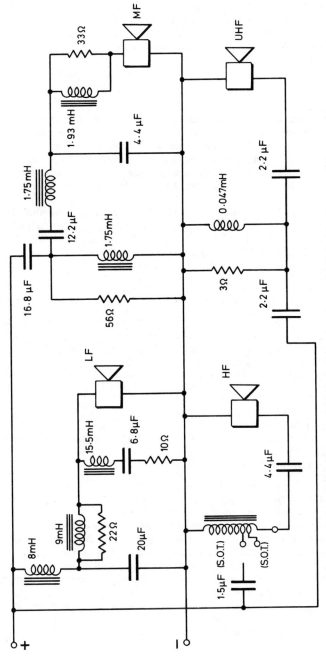

Figure 6.27 Commercial high performance four-way, 3rd order crossover (Spendor BC3). Crossover points at 500 Hz, 3 kHz, adjusted on test to match HF sensitivity. HF unit rolls off naturally above 14 kHz. LF is a 305 mm bextrene cone, MF a 200 mm bextrene cone, HF a 38 mm dome and UHF a 19 mm dome. See Figure 6.3. (Courtesy Spendor Ltd)

12 mm cores are satisfactory and the low power, two-way 25 W systems commonly utilise cores in the 9.5 mm diameter range.

Well designed conventional air-gapped transformer type cores are advisable when large inductance values with both low loss and high current ratings are required.

Capacitors

Electrolytic capacitors have acquired a poor reputation due to historically wide tolerances, poor stability and a high loss factor at the upper audio frequencies. These criticisms are no longer justified, since excellent electrolytic capacitors specifically designed for crossover use are now available. More recently high performance versions have been developed, which offer low loss and greatly improved tolerance and stability.

Life tests on normal grade (±20%) components have shown long term stability of better than ±2% (two years service), while for a premium they can be obtained to the 5% tolerance advisable for the more critical applications. In the case of high performance systems the capacitors may be selected to a 2.5% tolerance by the speaker manufacturer. The usual rating of 50 V a.c. which allows a reasonable safety margin with 8 Ω based systems, up to 150 W programme.

Where lower loss and even closer tolerances are required, plastic film capacitors provide the answer. Some varieties have the additional advantage of being self healing in the event of a transient voltage overload. Values of 20 μF and above are very costly, and are usually built up of combinations of smaller components. Nevertheless where a high quality, high power 50 μF or 80 μF capacitor is required, the only other solution is to employ one of the special types designed for power factor correction with power transmission networks.

While plastic film capacitors are widely used in critical applciations such as mid- and high-frequency crossover sections, the large values in the bass section are usually still electrolytic. At low frequencies the loss factor is usually more than adequate, and the internal resistance may be accounted for in the design.

Circuit geometry

Due to the presence of potentially high currents in the inductors and the mutual coupling of thoughtlessly orientated adjacent inductors components, the construction and layout of a crossover network is highly important. If inductors are closely spaced (separation less than 20 mm), they should always be positioned at right angles to minimise the interaction. If a printed circuit board is employed, the conductor foils should be of adequate breadth to ensure a low resistance, and in addition the track layout should be designed so that common return paths for the filter sections are avoided.

6.3 ACTIVE FILTER CROSSOVERS

The consumer market at present shows reluctance to accept loudspeakers which employ active crossovers with accompanying multiple power amplifiers though this is likely to be overcome in the future. However, in theory this technique offers the greatest scope for the advancement of the loudspeaker art, and a number of designs are already in production. Important benefits include: .

(1)   A reduction in intermodulation distortion in the accompanying amplifiers due to their operation over a narrower bandwidth.

(2)   Subjectively, the performance of well designed active systems exceeds expectation when comparison is made with the single amplifier/passive crossover alternative.   Characterisations of 'louder' and 'clearer' are frequently made, and are believed due to the reduction in 'stressful' loading on the individual amplifiers.   For example, when a main amplifier clips or enters distortion as may occur during a momentary powerful bass transient, the distortion harmonics will be clearly reproduced by the treble driver in a passive system.   In contrast the electronic configuration keeps the bass amplifier distortion to the bass driver, and the treble range remains clear and undistorted. (This is in fact a special case of the intermodulation improvement noted above.) This quality advantage still holds true for two-way systems with a typical crossover at 3 kHz, provided that the bass/mid unit has a reasonable intrinsic rolloff above the crossover point.   If not, a simple passive low-pass filter could be fitted between it and the respective drive amplifier.

(3)   Bass equalisation may be readily incorporated in the active crossover.   This is valuable if the low frequency alignment requires equalisation.

(4)   The association between driver and amplifier may be beneficially extended to include the LF driver in the feedback loop of the matching amplifier (this results in the so called 'motional feedback' or 'servo bass' designs).

(5)   Variations in driver sensitivity may be easily controlled via low-level gain control potentiometers.

(6)   Because each power amplifier feeds a single driver the overload protection thresholds may be more precisely set than is possible with the normal crossover and single 'universal' power amplifier.

(7)   The power amplifiers are directly connected across the terminals of each driver.   The units are thus driven from a constant voltage source which will tend to suppress the fundamental resonance via electromagnetic damping;(the degree depends on the driver Q. With treble units the absence of the usual series capacitor component in a matching passive crossover avoids the resonance problem previously discussed in Section 6.2,

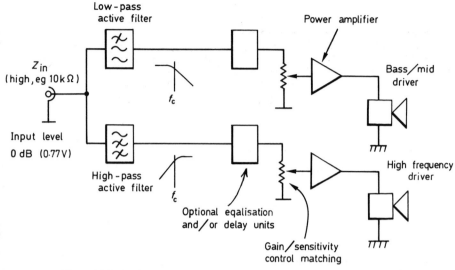

Figure 6.28   Basic two-way active crossover system

although the response fall-off due to the motor coil inductance will still remain.)

In addition, the amplifier output impedance can be made negative, if required, providing further control at the fundamental resonance.

(8)   Electronic filters provide a considerable variety of equalisation, response shape and phase characteristics which would be unwieldly if not impossible to realise with passive networks. In addition, electronic filters may be easily adjusted during production.

(9)   Delay stages may be provided electronically in the signal paths to specific drivers allowing equalisation of time delays which may exist between units in the system when optimally mounted. Such compensation is useful for the maintenance of symmetrical directivity in the lateral plane over the several important octaves near the crossover frequencies. Time-delay correction can also facilitate minimum phase design.[4]

(10)   Active filters potentially have lower distortion than passive ones, due to the elimination of cored inductors.

A full treatment of active filters is not within the scope of this book. Details of the subject are well covered[5] but some basic circuits will be examined here together with examples of current practice.

An active crossover system, Fig.6.28, consists of low-level filter sections, gain control and equalisation stages and a power amplifier for each filter/driver.

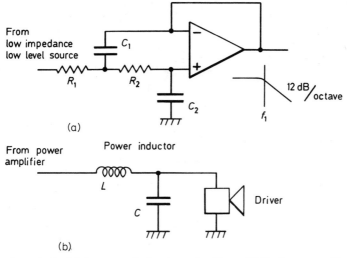

Figure 6.29   (a) Low-pass, 2nd order active filter.   (b) Passive power filter, 2nd order, low-pass

Theoretically an active filter is a more versatile device than its passive counterpart and response functions may be synthesised which would not only be difficult but might actually be impossible to realise with passive networks. Its great advantage lies in the elimination of the inductor which is the least satisfactory electrical component. With the use of integrated operational amplifier units and sensible value precision capacitors, for example, 10 nF to 1 μF, rather than the 1 μF to 100 μF required for the passive case, almost any filter characteristic may be readily and economically synthesised.

Second order low pass filters

Let us examine an active and a passive form of a low pass, 12 dB/octave filter with a 500 Hz cutoff frequency, f_C. In the active form a suitable network comprises a 741 integrated circuit amplifier together with two small capacitors and two resistors (Fig.6.29).

Though the cost of the power supplies cannot be ignored in the active case, it is usually shared with the power amplifiers and other sections of the crossover. The passive counterpart (Fig.6.31(b)), while avoiding complications of power supplies, conversely requires a large inductor, 2 mH for example, with a correspondingly large matching capacitor (Fig.6.29(b)). If the latter is built to the same stability and accuracy as the active filter component, the total cost may be several times greater than that of the active form.

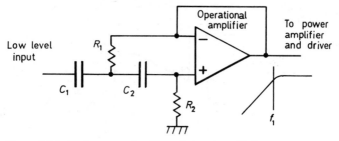

Figure 6.30 High pass active filter, 2nd order. If $R_1 = R_2$ and $C_1 = C_2$ = $1/2\pi RC$, $f_c = 1/(2\pi RC)$

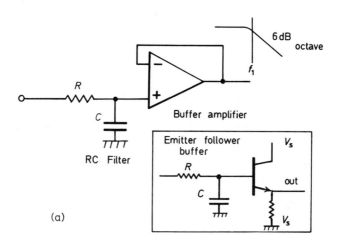

(a)

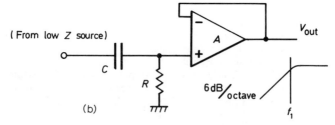

(b)

Figure 6.31 1st order RC filter; (a) low-pass form, (b) high-pass form (with buffer amplifier A)

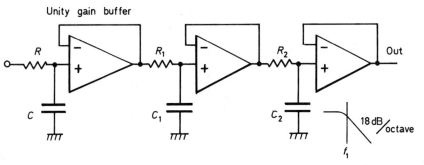

Figure 6.32   3rd order low pass filter, via cascaded 1st order sections (see also Fig.6.38)

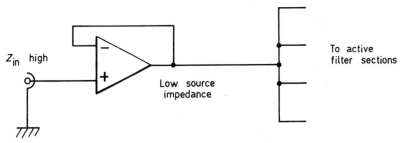

Figure 6.33   Input buffer (may be combined with audio bandpass input filter)

High pass filters

Figure 6.30 shows a high-pass second order form of Fig.6.29(a).

First-order low pass

Simpler first-order filters are conveniently obtained with RC networks using an operational amplifier as a high unit impedance, low output impedance buffer to preserve the theoretical responses. In less critical applications, a simple unity-gain transistor stage, the emitter follower, may be used (Fig.6.31).

Higher orders

Stages may be cascaded to provide almost any rolloff rate but the cumulative effect of the rolloff frequency error must be noted, each stage response being additive. This also provides a means of controlling the initial slope and shape of the response via the location of the individual −3 dB rolloff points (Fig.6.32).

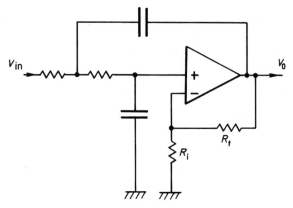

Figure 6.34   Active filter with gain. The passband gain $A = V_0/V_{in} = (R_f + R_i)/R_i$. *(If R_i is set, then $R_f = (A - 1)R_i$*

Driving impedance

All the filters should be driven from a low source, impedance. In a multiple way system, an additional input buffer amplifier (Fig.6.33) will provide this, as well as imparting high input impedance to the entire active filter system.

Equalisation for driver sensitivity and/or network losses

Combinations of passive and active RC networks may provide almost any required broad acting equalisation. Where considerable lift is necessary, the clipping headroom of the following power amplifier driving the loudspeaker must be considered, in the context of the spectral content of typical programme.

In an active crossover design, loss in the equaliser networks may be readily recovered by adding an amplification stage, or by adjusting the amplification of the corresponding op amps in the filter to some suitable low value (Fig.6.34).

The following are typical examples of equalisation.

Correction for rising driver axial response

Examining the circuit in Fig.6.35, at low frequencies below f_1, C represents a high impedance compared with R_3 and the network is essentially a resistive 'L' attenuator composed of R_1, R_2 and R_3. At high frequencies, above f_2, C is low in impedance compared with R_3 and R_2, and the attenuation is established by the 'L' attenuator R_1 and R_2. Between f_1 and f_2 the slope of the response may approach 6 dB/

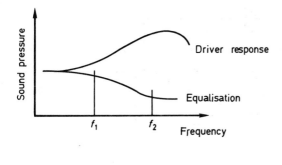

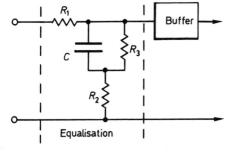

Figure 6.35   Equalisation of rising driver response

octave when R_2 is low and R_3 very high, and may be reduced by any degree through adjustment of R_2 and R_3. The approximate 4 dB/octave slope required by the above example is not difficult to achieve over a limited span.

If the second rolloff at f_2 is not required, then R_2 is simply reduced to zero.

Correction for premature driver rolloff

Premature driver-rolloff can be compensated by using a boost network such as that shown in Fig.6.36.

In this example, the network is simply a resistive attenuator composed of R_1 and R_2 at low frequencies where the impedance of C is high. At some frequency where the reactance of $C(Z_C = 1/2\pi f)$ equals R, the response will have risen by 3 dB and will continue to rise by 6 dB/octave thereafter. The slope may be reduced if necessary by adding a further resistor in series with C.

Other irregularities

With good quality drivers it should rarely be necessary to apply a correction slope steeper than 6 dB/octave, and in practice this equalisation usually is provided for final tuning and balancing, rather than drastic compensation.

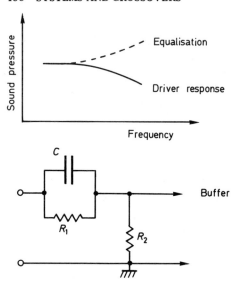

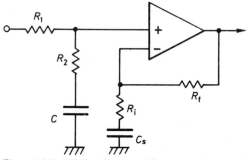

Figure 6.36   Equalisation of falling driver response

Figure 6.37   LF Equalisation. The attenuation produced by step-down response is compensated by the gain network R_f, R_i, in which incorporates C_s to provide a subsonic rolloff

Rather quicker acting equalisation may however be used, for example in conjunction with a calculated bass rolloff characteristic. A driver may be chosen on the basis of high mid-band efficiency which often implies a high Bl product with consequent overdamping at the bass resonance. Such a driver used in a sealed box might produce a system resonance at 40 Hz. Optimally damped, the output would be only -3 dB at that frequency. The large magnet, high efficiency model under consideration is however overdamped, such that a 6 dB loss at 40 Hz occurs, the response beginning to fall gently from as high as 100 Hz. The normal sealed-box rolloff of 12 dB/octave from 40 Hz has become a two stage slope, 6 dB/octave from 100 Hz to 50 Hz, and approaching 12 dB/octave

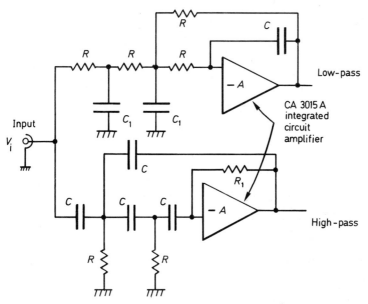

Figure 6.38   3rd order Butterworth crossover (after Ashley)[6]

$$\left.\frac{V_0}{V_i}\right|_{(LF)} = \frac{0.5}{s^3 + 2s^2 + 2s + 1} \; ; \quad \left.\frac{V_0}{V_i}\right|_{(HF)} = \frac{0.55^3}{s^3 + 2s^2 + 2s + 1}$$

with f_0 at 318 Hz,

$$R = 8.25 \text{ k}\Omega, \qquad R_1 = 90 \text{ k}\Omega$$
$$C = 0.022 \text{ }\mu\text{F}, \qquad C_1 = 0.15 \text{ }\mu\text{F}$$

below 40 Hz. If amplifier headroom and programme considerations permit, bass lift at a 6 dB/octave rate may be applied to restore the low frequency output. A suitable network is shown in Fig.6.37.

C_S is chosen to reduce the gain at subsonic frequencies (e.g. below 30 Hz) and hence to prevent the bass boost from continuing below that frequency.

More complex equalisation may be used along these lines, one commercial example forming a 10th order network in conjunction with the LF loudspeaker system.

Higher order filters by direct synthesis

Active filter theory is a versatile and powerful tool, and can provide numerous desirable filter characteristics.

Ashley et al. described a two-way third-order active Butterworth filter operating at 318 Hz which employed a single integrated circuit incorporating two operational amplifier blocks[6] (Fig.6.38).

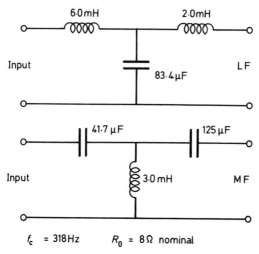

f_c = 318Hz R_0 = 8 Ω nominal

Figure 6.39   Passive, constant resistance Butterworth equivalent of Fig.6.38

With a total of count of 14 small components plus an integrated circuit, and assuming that the power supply is derived from an accompanying power amplifier, this realisation seems highly effective from both a cost and performance point of view.

This basic circuit may be scaled to fit almost any application. However a buffer amplifier stage is a worthwhile addition to drive the two filters, since the total input impedance is well below 10 kΩ.

This may be compared with the equivalent passive filter from Fig.6.39.

Another example of a 3-way active crossover circuit is given in Fig. 6.40 and a complete system in Fig.6.41. (See Appendix 3.)

Gain limitation in active filter amplifiers

The rolloff rate in an active filter is only maintained as long as there is sufficient gain present in the loop. If the gain is not constant with frequency, a situation likely to occur with one of the internally compensated op-amps when used at the higher audio frequencies, the loop gain might be insufficient to maintain the performance. Up to now the active filter treatment has assumed perfect op-amp performance, at least over the audio band. This implies that the characteristically high input impedance, low output impedance and high gain of such a block are uniform over the working frequency range. The 741 integrated circuit is adequate for low frequency work, but a wider bandwidth type is recommended for mid- and high-frequency use.

When working near gain limits, operational amplifiers will understandably produce higher distortion. Some also suffer from crossover

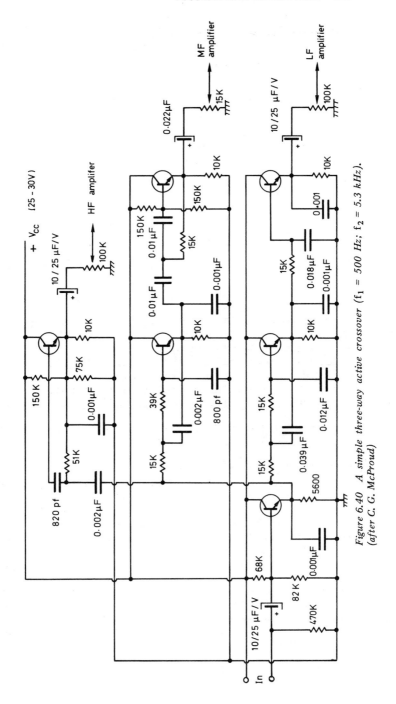

Figure 6.40 A simple three-way active crossover ($f_1 = 500$ Hz; $f_2 = 5.3$ kHz). (after C. G. McProud)

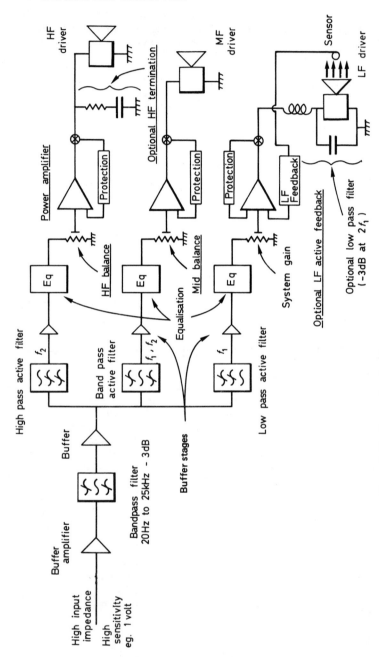

Figure 6.41 Comprehensive three-way electronic crossover system

effects, since class A/B output stages are often used. The existence of these distortions should be borne in mind, and for highly critical applications a designer may prefer to use special amplifier units or even discrete circuitry in his active filters.

Several commercial high performance active crossovers employ special class 'A' output, high-gain operational amplifier units of wide bandwidth and low distortion.

Loudspeaker system alignment

The ability to readily adjust the gain of the various sections of an active filter crossover to account for sensitivity variations in the drive units has already been mentioned. A further facility concerns individual tailoring of the response characteristics. A given equalisation may be correct for a typical driver but the performance spread in a batch of units may necessitate individual alignment. By judicious use of pre-set variable resistors in place of fixed equalisation components, provision for such adjustment is readily incorporated.

Maintenance and repair

Speaker systems designed for the most critical applications such as studio monitoring must be consistent. If a fault occurs, either due to a blown driver or electrical failure in the crossover, it must be possible to restore the system to the same standard of performance after repair.

The obvious penalty of an electronic crossover system is the degraded reliability when compared with its passive counterpart. The very presence of pre-set gain and equalisation controls adds to the problems, and also allows an inexperienced operator to misalign the system.

A recent active crossover design from the UK Company of Boothroyd-Stuart illustrates some of the precautions it is necessary to take to ensure a consistent performance. In this three-way system the drivers are pre-tested for sensitivity and response. Divided into groups for each system, each group is coded and the amplifier crossover matched to it. In the event of a driver failure, a matching coded unit may be used for replacement and if a fault develops in the crossover, a complete new panel is supplied, also pre-programmed to match the serial number code of the defective system.

An alternative approach would involve a careful alignment and calibration procedure for the electronics section, with the relevant code and level settings provided. The system could then be recalibrated via electrical rather than acoustic measurement in the event of a repair.

6.4 PASSIVE CROSSOVER CALCULATIONS

In concluding this chapter it is useful to consider a simple way of deriving numerical values for the 3rd order Butterworth crossover net-

TABLE 6.1

Frequency	C_1 (μF)	C_2 (μF)	C_3 (μF)	L_1 (mH)	L_2 (mH)	L_3 (mH)
250 Hz	160	50	80	8.2	5.1	2.6
350 Hz	114	36	57	5.8	3.6	1.8
500 Hz	66	21	33	3.4	2.1	1.1
1 kHz	40	12.4	20	2.0	1.3	0.64
3 kHz	13.2	4.1	6.6	0.68	0.42	0.21
5 kHz	8	2.5	4.0	0.41	0.26	0.13
7.5 kHz	5.3	1.7	2.7	0.27	0.17	0.085

These values are for 8 Ω systems but may be scaled to any frequency or impedance.

work. The 3rd order Butterworth crossover in Fig.6.42 may be scaled to any required frequency by simple multiplication since the values are inversely proportional to frequency. The set values refer to 1 kHz with nominally 8 Ω drivers. To readjust for 4 Ω systems, the capacitance values are doubled and the inductors halved. For 16 Ω systems the inductance values are doubled and the capacitors halved.

For 2 kHz the values are halved, for 200 Hz all values are multiplied by 10, etc.

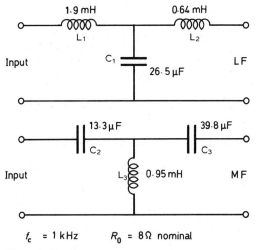

f_c = 1 kHz R_0 = 8 Ω nominal

Figure 6.42

Final system response conformity with the theory relies on the driver input impedance being nominally resistive and constant, and also that the amplitude/frequency response be uniform.

The alternative 'M' derived values for the circuit in Fig.6.42 are given in Table 6.1.

REFERENCES

1. Harwood, H. D., 'Some aspects of loudspeaker quality', *Wireless World,* May (1976)
2. Hughes, F. M. (a pseudonym for M. Colloms), 'A group test of thirty pairs of commercial loudspeakers', *Hi Fi For Pleasure,* 4, July, September and October (1976)
3. Benson, J. E., 'An introduction to the design of filtered loudspeakers systems', *J. Audio Engng Soc.,* 23, No.7 (1975)
4. Linkwitz, S. H., 'Active crossover networks for non-coincident drivers', *J. Audio Engng Soc.,* 24, No.1 (1976)
5. Allen, P. E., 'Practical considerations of active filter design', *J. Audio Engng Soc.* 22, No.10 (1974)
6. Ashley, J. R. and Henne, L. M., 'Operational amplifier implementation of ideal electronic crossover networks', *J. Audio Engng Soc.,* 19, No.1 (1971)
7. Colloms, M., 'Some practical aspects of loudspeaker design relating to perceived stereo image quality', *Hi-fi News,* 24, No.6 (1979)

BIBLIOGRAPHY

Ashley, J. R. and Kaminsky, A. L., 'Active and passive filters as loudspeaker crossover networks', *J. Audio Engng Soc.,* 19, No.6 (1971)

Cooke, R., 'Monitoring loudspeakers', *Hi Fi News,* London

Hilliard, J. K. and Kimball, H. R., 'Dividing networks for loudspeaker systems', *J. Audio Engng Soc.,* 26, No.11 (1978)

KEF Electronics Ltd., 'Model 105', *Keftopics,* 3, No.1 (1978)

King, M. W., 'Activating your loudspeaker crossover', *Audio,* USA, April (1972)

Linkwitz, S. H., 'Loudspeaker system design', *Wireless World,* 84, No.1516 (1978)

Linkwitz, S. H., 'Passive crossover networks for non-coincident drivers', *J. Audio Engng Soc.,* 26, No.3 (1978)

Read, D. C., 'Active crossover networks', *Wireless World,* 574–6, December (1973) and 443–8, November (1974)

Rettinger, M., *Practical Electroacoustics,* Thames & Hudson, London (c. 1955)

Small, R. H., 'Constant voltage crossover network design', *J. Audio Engng Soc.* 19, No.1 (1971)

—, 'Speaker Crossover Networks', *Electronics Today International,* p.64 et seq., October (1972)

Thiele, A. N., 'Air cored inductors for audio', *J. Audio Engng Soc.,* 24, No.5 (1976)

Thiele, A. N., 'Another look at crossover networks', *Audio* (USA), August (1978)

Wall, P. K., 'Active and passive crossover networks with no transient distortion', *Proc. Audio Engng Soc. 50th Convention,* London, March (1975)

— 'Active loudspeaker crossover filter', *Elector,* 3, No.6 (1977)

7

The enclosure

The enclosure is simply a structure which supports the loudspeaker drive units, and may provide designed acoustic properties of radiation pattern and driver acoustic loading. The term is usually taken as referring to an enclosed box where some form of loading is applied to the bass driver. However, an enclosure can be open backed or else conceal a horn or other system folded into a compact structure.

In practice the enclosure exerts a considerable influence over the sound of a complete system. A moving coil driver radiates energy by vibrating a diaphragm assembly whose reaction will simultaneously excite the driver chassis causing it to vibrate in sympathy. The chassis must therefore be rigidly clamped to a strong panel to prevent it from moving, and hence reducing the cone output (Section 7.10). Nevertheless, some energy will inevitably be imparted to the panel. To this may be added the sound energy radiated from the diaphragm incident upon the panel. If this energy is not dissipated, the resonant modes of the enclosure may be audible and 'colour' the overall sound of the system.

7.1 ENCLOSURE MATERIALS

A simple box structure will possess a series of resonant modes due to torsion and panel flexure, their frequency and magnitude dependent on the 'Q' of the material and also its thickness and density. As resonant modes are less likely to be excited with increased panel thickness and density, they will become correspondingly less obvious, and thus it is well worth noting the relative densities of the various materials used in cabinet construction (Table 7.1).

Wood

Traditionally most loudspeaker enclosures have been constructed from wood. It has many advantages, not the least of which is that from its mass, it is relatively non-resonant. Most countries have an established cabinet industry, often linked with furniture manufacturers, and thus

TABLE 7.1. THE DENSITIES OF MATERIALS USED IN LOUDSPEAKER
ENCLOSURE WALLS

Material		Density (kg/m^3)
Lead		11.3×10^3
Steel		7.7×10^3
Mazak		6.0×10^3
Aluminium		2.6×10^3
Concrete		2.6×10^3
Brick		1.8×10^3
Sand		1.5×10^3
Chipboard		0.81×10^3
Oak		0.72×10^3
Plywood	(Depends on grade)	0.67×10^3
Mahogany		0.67×10^3
Pine		0.45×10^3
Celotex or fibre board		0.32×10^3
Polyethylene (approx.)	(Depends on molecular weight)	1.0×10^3
Bituminous damping	(Depends on grade)	$1.0–3.0 \times 10^3$

enclosures can usually be supplied at a realistic price with a wide range
of wood grades and thicknesses to choose from. It is an easy material
to work with and historically labour costs were relatively low.

Chipboard is the densest of all the wood materials, and as it comes
in reasonably priced, uniform sheets which resist warping and can be
easily veneered, it is not surprising that the great majority of wood cabinets today are constructed from this material. The thickness used is
scaled to the volume of cabinet required. Below 30 litres, 12 mm is
suitable, while a 30—60 litre enclosure generally employs 18 mm, and
larger cabinets, 25 mm. Chipboard is also available in various densities,
the grade known as '600' being the one generally employed; preferably
in 'three layer' variety, with fine texture outer skins covering a coarser
interior. This has the lowest flexural 'Q' of almost any undamped wood
material.

Other woods may also be employed for enclosure construction, the
results depending on the grade selected and the size of cabinet involved.
Solid woods such as well seasoned afromosia have been used in the past,
and high quality birch plywood is also frequently encountered as an
alternative to chipboard, although both its 'Q' and more particularly
its cost are greater.

Concrete

With enclosure of very high mass such as those built of thick concrete or
brick, it is difficult to excite the resonant modes. However such enclo-

sures are generally assembled on-site and as such are not practicable for normal manufacture and supply. However, in the past thin-wall cast concrete enclosures have been suggested but unfortunately the effect of reducing the wall thickness means that the advantage of high mass is lost, and the enclosure will thus prove quite resonant, and will have poor resistance to impact. It is however possible to produce a successful concrete enclosure through choice of suitable filler and additives to reduce the 'Q' and by employing suitably designed internal strengthening beams cast into the structure to control the resonant modes.

Other materials

Providing that the structure is well damped there is no objection to using metal for cabinet construction, and a few high quality designs have been produced that employ steel or aluminium alloy front panels. Welded steel enclosures have been used for systems that are subject to arduous duty, such as in the field of public address.

Moulded plastic cabinets will make increasing economic sense for quantity production, in view of the accelerating price costs of both labour and natural wood. In fact, further research in cooperation with major producers is urgently required to develop suitable synthetics that possess the necessary acoustic properties and can be easily moulded into cabinet shells. For example, certain grades of expanded polyurethane have been tried by several manufacturers, noteably, B. & O., Wharfedale and KEF.

Another promising material is polyester resin, highly loaded with a heavy mineral powder. When mixed with up to 70% by weight of ground limestone, excellent acoustic properties below 1 kHz are demonstrated. Recently aluminium has been utilised both in a thin-wall bitumous damped form and box section extrusions for the smaller enclosures.

7.2 ENCLOSURE RESONANCES

The volume resonances of a box enclosure system, including the Helmholtz resonances, are dealt with under the chapter on acoustic loading. The following discussion concerns those internal and undesired resonances which may contribute to colouration.

Unless an enclosure is spherical or ellipsoidal, all or some of its sides will consist of plane surfaces clamped at their edges. Such a clamped panel will have its own acoustic output when forming part of an energised loudspeaker, derived from sound energy within the enclosure. The output consists of standing-wave modes at higher frequencies and pressure modes at those frequencies where the wavelengths exceed the internal enclosure dimensions. Adjacent panels may be similarly excited by vibrational energy from the drive unit chassis.

Theoretically a clamped panel has a well defined vibrational series in both longitudinal (volume stiffness) and bending modes. A further mode is due to the panel mass resonating with its own and the enclosure's air volume stiffness. Stevens[1] found that in a typical reflex cabinet this latter resonance appeared at almost twice the fundamental enclosure resonance, a condition verified over a range of tuned system frequencies. The resonances of a flat panel, edge clamped, are given by[2]

$$f_\mathrm{r} = 0.48 \left[Ct \cdot \left(\frac{A}{L^2} + \frac{B}{W^2} \right) \right]$$

where A, B are the respective mode orders, t = the panel thickness in metres, C = the velocity of longitudinal sound waves in the material, and L, W are the panel dimensions.

The other series is given by

$$f_\mathrm{r} = \frac{nC}{2l}$$

where C = velocity of sound in the panel, l = panel dimension related to mode calculated, and n = an integer from 1 to infinity.

The resonances of coupled panels in a finished enclosure are highly complex and are not amenable to analysis as in the case of a single panel. It is thus not possible to predict how coloured a given cabinet will be, as small variations in dimensions can give quite different results.

7.3 MAGNITUDE OF UNDAMPED PANEL OUTPUT

Many speaker designers have laboured by trial and error to control cabinet resonance by such methods as the use of high density constructional materials and internal bracing, or loading the panels with ceramic tiles and sand. However, their efforts have met with only moderate success.

Sand is an awkward medium to work with as it requires a retaining panel to hold it in place and has the further undesirable effect of causing the weight of an enclosure to soar dramatically. However, this treatment can be quite effective due to the added mass and also to the loss imparted by the vibration of the individual particles.

Rank's Leak/Wharfedale division hold a patent for an intriguing variation on the theme of filled cabinets, namely a water 'sandwich!' The enclosure is presumably a double skinned synthetic moulding, the intention being that the purchaser should fill the cabinet on delivery. An obvious advantage for the manufacturer is the greatly reduced transit weight of the partially completed system.

Resonant modes can be modified by increasing the thickness of the panels or by attaching battens to them, but although these measures may displace the resonances to more subjectively acceptable frequencies, they usually have little or no effect on their magnitude. Beam coupling of two opposite panels will only effect the fundamental bending reso-

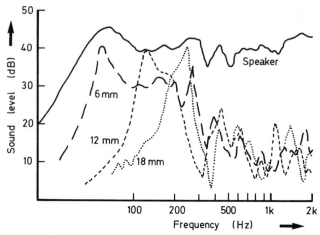

Figure 7.1   *Sound output of Birch-ply panels (after Barlow)*[3]

nance, where a major stiffening will result, suppressing this mode. Barlow[3] measured the sound output of square birch-ply panels excited by a driver mounted on the inside surface. A remarkable discovery was made, namely that the output at certain of the resonances approached the level achieved by the driver with the panel absent, thus indicating that the panel was almost wholly acoustically transparent at these frequencies (Fig.7.1).

However this is an exaggerated case as enclosure panels tend to be rectangular rather than square, and the listener is rarely on the panel axis. Nevertheless Stevens[1] has shown that for a typical 50 litre enclosure built of 18 mm chipboard, radiation from an undamped rear panel may have peaks which are only 10 dB below the front axial output (Fig.7.2).

In a normal sound field the output of the six cabinet walls will contribute to the desired forward radiation, and Harwood has noted a working '*Q*' of up to 100 in cabinet panels made from several varieties of wood. Subjectively derived evidence has shown that these resonances are clearly audible, and may have delay times of half a second or more. Clearly the choice of panel material alone is not likely to reduce either the '*Q*' or the reverberation time to a level where it becomes unobtrusive.

7.4 AUDIBILITY OF RESONANCE

It is worth noting that research conducted into the audibility of resonances relative to a given response curve, indicates that low '*Q*' resonances can be the most obvious, *Q* = 1 being the critically prominent

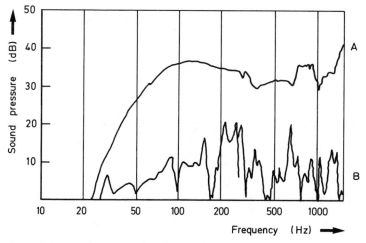

Figure 7.2   A: frontal output of cabinet; B: sound output from rear panel of cabinet (after Stevens)[1]

value[4]. Although this might seem to contradict the findings above, the two can in fact be viewed as separate and distinct cases. The audibility threshold work was done using a single resonance, whereas the enclosure effects represent a series of resonances. The word 'series' is highly relevant in this context, where it refers to a regular mathematically related sequence. It would appear that the human ear is highly sensitive to response irregularities based on a series[5], the latter being an accurate term to use when defining enclosure resonances. Fryer[4] has shown that under optimum conditions, a resonance whose amplitude is 20 dB below the steady state curve is detectable in classical music, and up to 30 dB below in steady noise excitation. This is confirmed in Steven's work[1] as well as by other practical conducted on test enclosures (see p.190).

7.5 RESONANCE CONTROL AND DAMPING MATERIALS

If a method of resonance control or 'damping' is applied, the 'Q' of the intrinsic panel resonance can be greatly reduced and hence the choice of panel material is of little consequence. This means that previously little used substances, such as injection moulded plastics, can be employed for cabinet construction.

Whereas in the case of a single enclosure high mass was a positive advantage, with the damped cabinet it is actually detrimental. Resonance control employs the principle of dissipation through friction. A given panel should be laminated with a special layer of comparable mass

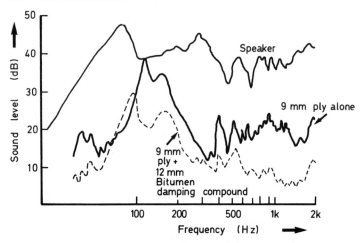

Figure 7.3   Two results are apparent from the application of damping. First, the amplitude of the resonances has been lowered by about 10 dB, and second, the added mass has somewhat reduced the fundamental panel resonant frequency. This in itself can prove advantageous, as the resonances which are likely to occur in the critical mid-band may as a result be shifted to a less aurally sensitive region (after Barlow)[3]

per unit area, this mass equivalence ensuring that a good mechanical match is achieved between the two layers to permit the effective transfer of vibrational energy from panel to the damping material. The layer is often a bituminous impregnated felt or card used for vibration control (largely in connection with automobile body panels). These materials have a high frictional loss in bending. A thin enclosure of low mass is clearly more effectively controlled by a given density of damping pad than is a thick one (Fig.7.3 and Fig.7.4).

Fairly pure lead sheeting is effective material for use in loading and damping enclosure walls, as it has exceptionally high density and plasticity. Its main drawback is its high cost, although it could well prove worthwhile for small cabinets of moderate internal volume. Certain grades of heat cured polyurethane (monothane) are potentially effective vibration absorbers. Other damping materials include Celotex or fibreboard, which is generally attached to a panel using a flexible adhesive such as PVA, and will produce some damping, particularly of the higher frequencies. Automobile underseal loaded with a sand filler is also fairly effective if applied thickly. However a word of caution is necessary with these latter substances. They rarely dry out completely and can contain a volatile solvent which may soften the cones and bonding of plastic drive units. This may result in a premature failure of the adhesive holding the cone and surround together, leading to the disintegration of the unit.

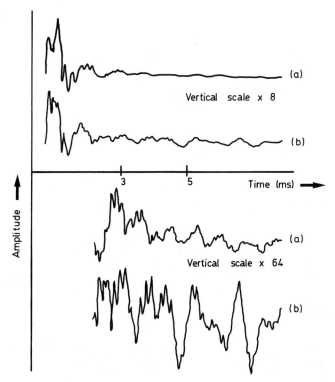

Figure 7.4   This shows two contrasting delayed impulse responses for a 100 mm plastic bass mid-range drive unit in a 7 litre closed box. The output is that which is mainly heard through the cone, although the panels also make some contribution.   Curve (a) employs a 12 mm chipboard construction with 12 mm of bituminous panel damping applied; Curve (b) uses hardboard of 6 mm thickness with no damping (courtesy KEF Electronics)

One of the more recent advances in the area of panel damping materials was made in 1972, when a patent was filed in Germany for a synthetic medium consisting of a heavy mineral-loaded thermoplastic. Dunlop (UK) have also investigated damping systems, and have found a soft foam sheet with a high mass counterlayer very effective[6,7] (Fig.7.5 and Tables 7.2 to 7.5).

Placement of damping pads

The dense damping pads appear to work by a combination of bending loss due to panel flexure and by the absorption of surface waves in the panel. A well built enclosure will have strengthened corners and seams,

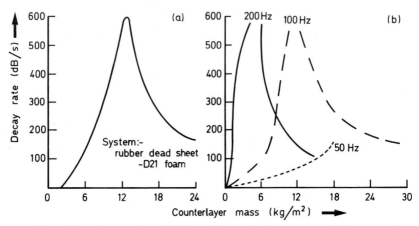

Figure 7.5   Decay rate variation with counter layer mass and frequency in laminated damping layers (rubber counterlayers on foam base) (after Payne, Wilson and Wragg)[7]

TABLE 7.2.   RESULTS OF DECAY RATE vs SURFACE DENSITY USING SAMPLES 1.6 mm THICK

Material	Surface density (kg/m^2)	Decay rate (dB/s) Free	Decay rate (dB/s) Bonded
Aluminium	0.66	10	4.5
Polyurethane 'Chipfoam'	1.27	44	1.5
Felt	1.58	30	2.5
Latex foam	1.63	22	6
PVC/plasticiser/china clay (100/75/200)	2.50	40	3
PVC/plasticiser/whiting (100/75/200)	2.51	13	2
'Dead sheet'	4.8	50	2
PVC/plasticiser/molybdenum powder (100/75/500)	5.0	59	2
Lead sheet	14.7	164	15

TABLE 7.3.   COMMERCIALLY-AVAILABLE DAMPING PRODUCTS

Material	Surface density (kg/m^2)	Temperature $(°C)$	Decay rate (dB/s)
Bitumen	1.48	Ambient	4
		+5	5.5
Coumarone indene resin	1.45	Ambient	5.5
		+50	10.5
Polyethylacrylate/c. black*	1.45	Ambient	2
		−10	23.5

TABLE 7.4. PERFORMANCE OF FOAMS

Foam code	Type	Bulk density IYM		Bulk stiffness (kN/m^2)	Decay rate (dB/s)	Perfor- mance
		(kg/m^3)	(MN/m^2)			
	Test bar	–	–	–	2	poor
D7	Polyether	21.5	20.6	12.9	3.5	poor
DE300	Polyether	23.4	11.7	10.8	4.5	poor
S12	Polyether	29.3	6.0	5.1	4.0	poor
D1	Polyether	16.5	18.9	4.9	5.5	poor

TABLE 7.5. ATTENUATING PROPERTIES

Counterlayer	Foam layer	Decay rate (dB/s) at 100 Hz	
		Bonded	Non-Bonded
Rubber (4.9 kg/m^2)	D7 Polyurethane foam	3.5	183
Rubber (4.9 kg/m^2)	D21 Polyurethane foam	214	186
Rubber (4.9 kg/m^2)	SBR Latex foam	236	150

TABLE 7.6. EFFECT OF VARYING FOAM THICKNESS (D21 FOAM)

Foam thickness (mm)	Decay rate (dB/s) at 100 Hz
2	7.5
4	34
6	51
8	190
10	407
12	194

and hence the panel edges will possess a high mechanical impedance where the absorption will be poor. Harwood[5] suggests that a 50% control layer coverage of a panel in the central area will produce the most effective damping for a given quantity of material.

7.6 STANDING-WAVE MODES

The peaky nature of the sound output from a panel is exacerbated by the presence of a series of discrete standing-wave modes inside a plain rectangular enclosure. These standing waves are well defined and may be responsible for distinct 'sub-colouration'. In the case of a small enclosure, this is effectively characterised by the use of the term 'boxiness'.

The standing-wave frequencies are given by Rayleigh:

$$f_r = (C/2) \; [(A/L)^2 + (B/W)^2 + (D/H)^2]^{1/2}$$

where C = velocity of sound in air, A, B and D are the mode orders, and L, W and H are the internal cabinet dimensions.

Several steps may be taken to reduce or control standing waves. The first is to avoid symmetry in cabinet construction; for example, the worst case is an enclosure where all panel dimensions are equal. In the field of room acoustics, ratios have been calculated to provide the minimum excitation of standing-wave modes, the room dimensions being 2.3:1.6:1.0, these equally valid in the context of loudspeaker enclosures.

While parallel-piped or conventional rectangular enclosures are the general rule, a cabinet with anti-parallel sides will stagger the modes and hence reduce the internal resonances. For example, it is often beneficial to design the sub-enclosure for an open backed mid-range unit so that the plane of the rear panel is angled with respect to the front, as this will help to suppress the main front/back reflection. Long tubes have also been used with success in this application; well packed with absorbent they form a graded termination to the rear cone energy. Cylindrical cabinets have the particular advantage of a very high radial stiffness, and hence their panel colouration is considerably lower than a rectangular enclosure of similar wall thickness[3]. Even if a cabinet has dimensions that are inharmonically related, as recommended above, the magnitude of the standing-wave resonances can still be appreciable.

A test enclosure of internal dimensions 57.0 × 32.0 × 26.6 cm, 48 litres in volume, and tuned to 40 Hz by a tube 20.3 cm long and 5.1 cm internal diameter, possessed prominent standing-wave modes at 300 Hz, 510 Hz and 620 Hz with a typical 'Q' of 40. The duct had its own tube resonance at 750 Hz, ($Q = 40$), in addition to the fundamental bass resonance at 40 Hz ($Q = 1.5$). To control such resonances, internal treatment by acoustic absorption is essential in a high performance system.

Suitable materials include lossy fibre blankets such as fibreglass and mineral or rockwool pads, plus polyester, cellulose and bonded acetate fibre wadding, the latter commonly known as BAF. Speaker enclosures of the sealed-box variety may employ self supporting volume fillers such as wool-felt, resin-bonded fibreglass or long-haired wool, these also providing a degree of damping at the fundamental resonance.

However if a speaker is optimally designed, little or no damping of the fundamental resonance should be required as this factor will have been accounted for in the driver system analysis. In such a case, the absorbent wadding need only be fixed to the enclosure walls, a well bonded material such as BAF or polyester wadding being the most suitable. Thick carpet-felt is also effective.

High level non linearity is common with linings which can move at low frequencies. This can be seen as a discrepancy in the amplitude/frequency responses taken under steady state and transient conditions[10].

In recent years, open-cell synthetic foams have found favour, in particular certain acoustically absorbent grades of polyurethane. This material is also used for absorption wedges in many anechoic chambers. In small enclosures 12—18 mm thicknesses are effective and in the larger designs of 60—100 litre volume, blocks 50 mm thick are usually satisfactory. Some manufacturers have also used foam sheets with a wedged surface moulded into the structure. (Synthetic foams may represent a fire hazard, and the location of the crossover and adjacent linings deserves consideration.)

Optimum placement of absorbent

The region of maximum standing-wave energy is in the enclosure 'volume' rather than at the sides, and thus the absorption material is ideally placed in the cabinet 'space' rather than attached as sheets to the inside surface of the panels.

7.7 DRIVER-CONE TRANSMISSION OF INTERNAL RESONANCES

Standing-wave modes and volume resonances may not only be heard via the cabinet panels but also through a driver cone. A thick, heavy cone will be less acoustically transparent than a thin one. Furthermore the output from a cone will be proportional to its area, a small cone allowing less of the internal cabinet energy to escape. With large cones, in shallow enclosures, where the front to rear mode is strong and relatively high in frequency, a layer of absorption immediately behind the driver has proved beneficial, and additional acoustic obstructions such as polystyrene sections have been attached to larger cones to increase their opacity.

A speaker cone will obey the mass law for sound transmission above a certain break frequency around 5 kHz, and the transmission is fairly constant at lower frequencies except where resonances occur. In the example given in Fig.7.6, longitudinal modes in the cone area are attributed to the poor attenuation in the 1—5 kHz region, while the average loss is 16—18 dB. At the driver's fundamental resonance the attenuation will of course approach zero. (Figure 7.7 shows a transmitted box reflection.)

7.8 CABINET CONSTRUCTION

Cabinet size

The unwanted sound output of a cabinet structure is proportional to its surface area. Small cabinets are less of a problem in this respect and

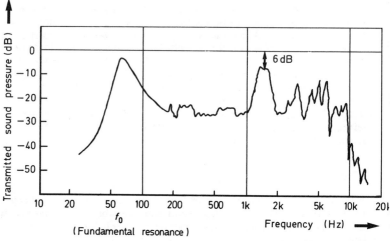

Figure 7.6   *Transmission curve of a 170 mm chassis bextrene cone driver (after Fryer)*

hence panel damping is not so critical. Conversely such an enclosure will, by comparison with larger cabinets, suffer from internal reflection modes of both higher Q and frequency. These observations suggest that for rigid enclosures of up to 15 litres, internal volume absorption is important, while for larger sizes, the increasing panel surface area means that panel damping assumes greater significance.

Large enclosures of 60—100 litres volume utilising the thin-wall, highly damped technique, may suffer a lack of rigidity at low frequencies, due to the flexure of the large panel area absorbing bass energy at the main enclosure volume resonance. With medium sized 40—50 litre enclosures there may need to be a compromise between mid-frequency colouration and cabinet rigidity at low frequencies. Cross-bracing is useful for increasing the wall stiffness of such a cabinet without greatly modifying the colouration characteristics. Front to back bracing is also worth employing where the front panel is weakened by a significant area of drive unit aperture.

Corner joints

Modern cabinet making techniques can produce accurate mitred joints with the use of 'V' groove cutting machines, and a speaker designer may be tempted to accept these as satisfactory. While this may hold true in the case of small, thick walled enclosures, a more substantial edge clamping technique is required for larger cabinets. The success of panel damping to some extent depends upon the rigid coupling of adjacent panels, so that one helps to dissipate energy in the other. The front panel is often weakened by both drive unit apertures and ports, and as it is usually undamped, it must be rigidly coupled to the enclosure shell in order to adequately transfer and dissipate the unwanted energy.

In an enclosure, all internal seams should have well glued battens or corner pieces made from a tough grade of wood about 18 mm in cross-section. However, chipboard or plywood offcuts are also suitable, the aim being to increase the adhesive contact area between adjacent panels at the seam. If the front or rear panels are removeable, (many modern designs have permanently fixed panels with access to the crossover and wiring obtained through the bass unit aperture), a generous quantity of screws should be employed to securely clamp down the panels.

Front grilles

Most loudspeakers have some sort of acoustically transparent covering to protect the drive unit diaphragms and to screen them from view, although with a few domestic designs the visual effect of the drivers has been exploited and a grille omitted. Likewise many professional systems, particularly the horn types, do not require protection, nor are visual considerations very important in this context.

The grille material can have a considerable effect on sound quality and must be carefully selected. A less than acoustically transparent covering will not only absorb sound energy, particularly in the treble range, but will also provide a partially reflecting surface adjacent to the drivers, thus producing further colouration. It is not easy to produce a material which is sufficiently transparent in acoustic terms and visually opaque. Light machine-knitted 'stretch' polyester fabrics are suitable and special plastic monofilament woven materials are also produced.

This problem is alleviated if the contrast of the driver panel assembly is reduced; for example, by painting both the drivers and the panel black. If a fabric is employed it must be firmly attached under tension spaced from the accompanying panel, or it may flap and produce spurious noises. A thin layer of open-cell foam, approximately 4—6 cm thick, may be fitted under the grille cloth at its perimeter in order to space the fabric away from the driver panel and impart some resilient tensioning.

An additional complication arises with a reflex enclosure which has a high air velocity at the port opening, as the close proximity of a decorative grille fabric may well disturb its operation.

The fabric is usually stretched over a light wood or metal frame, whose side members should be as large as possible, since the fabric tension can easily warp a frail structure. The 'step' which results from positioning the produced grille baffle adjacent to the drive units must be given due consideration so that the reflections do not cause colouration and disturb the polar response.

More recently, large pore open cell foam slabs have been used in place of fabric grilles, and while these have a remarkably low loss on axis, off axis some reduction of treble energy can occur, due to the sound traversing a thicker section of material. This could conceivably prove an advantage with some drivers, where the off-axis polar response needs to be curtailed. The appeal of foam grilles is largely aesthetic, as a wide range of surface contours and colours are available. Their self-supporting nature means that they can be directly fixed to the cabinet by means of a suitable grade of multi-hook plastic strip such as 'Velcro'. A further advantage concerns the fact that the 'step' of a wooden grille frame is avoided.

Fabricated grilles of wood slats are generally unsatisfactory, since they tend to act as diffraction gratings, but open-weave metal mesh has been successfully employed, and if backed with a thin black fabric can be visually effective.

7.9 DIFFRACTION AND CABINET SHAPE

Because of diffraction effects, the properties, size and surface irregularities of a baffle or enclosure will have a considerable influence on both the measured and subjective performance of a system. At low frequencies where wavelengths are long, even a large enclosure presents a relatively small obstacle to the radiated energy, and hence through diffraction, the output is uniformly propagated around the cabinet; i.e. the radiation pattern is virtually omni-directional.

Common rectangular enclosures

With increasing frequency a region is attained where the frontal dimensions of an enclosure become comparable with the wavelength of the sound being reproduced. The enclosure then begins to increasingly direct the sound energy into the frontal or forward plane.

At still higher frequencies the radiation pattern is theoretically hemispherical, bounded by the front panel plane, but in practice it is usually narrower, due to the inherent dispersion pattern of the drive units themselves (Fig.7.8).

This characteristic change in radiation pattern with frequency will vary with the size and shape of the enclosure involved. This behaviour is now examined in greater detail.

The 6 dB response step

Consider an ideal piston drive unit which possesses a theoretical uniform response when mounted in an infinite baffle. If positioned on the front face of a tall tubular enclosure, the resulting axial response would exhibit a distinct step of 6 dB at the transition between omnidirectional radiation at the lower frequencies and forward directed hemispherical radiation at higher frequencies. This irregularity is difficult to equalise and

Cumulative decay spectra

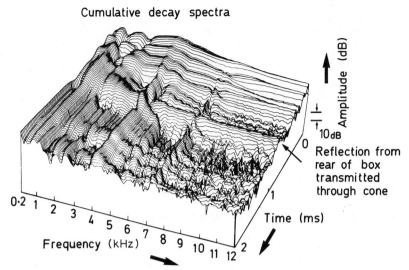

Figure 7.7   Output of 110 mm moving coil bass/mid range unit in 7 litre closed box showing ridge at t = 0.9 ms due to box reflection (courtesy KEF Electronics)

in consequence this cabinet shape is avoided by designers. Olsen's[8] classic set of responses for an identical driver in a series of cabinets shows that the 6 dB step is not present at a single frequency but appears as a series of ripples in the response curve at a multiple of the basic frequency, with a peak to peak amplitude as high as 10 dB (Fig.7.9).

These curves are valuable to all designers who seek to experiment with unusual cabinet shapes. Olsen appears to have tried most of them, and the resulting responses are worthy of closer inspection. 'A', the sphere, undoubtedly gives the smoothest characteristic. This is not surprising, as its shape is free from sharp discontinuities in the path of the expanding sound field. However, it is possible to achieve a reasonably smooth response with enclosures built of plane panels providing that they are based on an unequal length, width and height ratios, and preferably have chamfered or rounded front edges to eliminate the usual sharp profile (shape 'L', Fig.7.9).

The frequencies at which these major diffraction irregularities occur depends on the cabinet size. Small bookshelf systems might primarily exhibit the effect from 1 to 2 kHz, whereas it would be more prominent from 200 to 800 Hz in the case of large free standing enclosures. The pattern is also dramatically affected by position; for example, by placing a cabinet against a solid boundary such as a wall or floor.

It might even be possible to make some nominal correction to the axial response of an imperfect driver by suitable choice of cabinet size and proportion, so that the resulting diffraction effects help to equalise the driver.

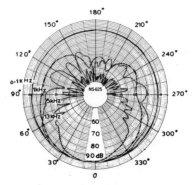

Figure 7.8   Polar diagram from a 30 litre, two-unit system containing a 200 mm cone driver working up to 2 kHz, and a 45 mm dome treble unit. The cabinet measures 500 cm × 280 cm × 249 cm.   The drivers are vertically mounted, with the polar plot taken in the horizontal, i.e. lateral plane. At 100 Hz the output at both the front and the rear is comparable as the cabinet dimensions are much less than a wavelength. At 1 kHz, the cabinet width approximates to a wavelength, and the rear energy output is well down at −25 dB, the cabinet showing a hemispherical pattern with increasing frequency.   However, by 15 kHz, the polar pattern is in fact controlled by the high frequency unit whose diaphragm diameter is the dominant factor. (Courtesy Yamaha)

Minimisation of diffraction

In choosing a suitable cabinet shape, asymmetrical placement of the drive units is beneficial as it results in unequal path lengths from the drivers to the edge of the enclosure.

Some drive units will have a relatively narrow dispersion in the midband which directs the energy clear of the cabinet edge and hence avoids diffraction effects at these frequencies. A typical plastic-coned bass mid-range unit working up to 2 or 3 kHz in a medium sized enclosure (40 litres) will have an off axis response which falls rapidly above 700 Hz and hence avoids cabinet edge diffraction effects which might otherwise be expected at the higher frequencies.

The most pronounced mid-band diffraction effects occur with small 50 mm dome radiators whose dispersion is almost hemispherical up to 2 kHz. With these units and also in the case of small dome tweeters, a plane surface free of obstruction, cavities or steps is essential if irregularities in the axial frequency response caused by diffraction are to be avoided. This applies also to the design of the front plates and mounting chassis of such radiators, which should present a smooth contour from the edge of the dome to the front panel surface. Even the projecting screw-heads on the chassis can cause measureable changes at the higher frequencies. Cabinet edge diffraction may also be controlled by judicious use of absorbent felt rings or similar structures placed around the driver to absorb side radiation and avoid cabinet edge effects.

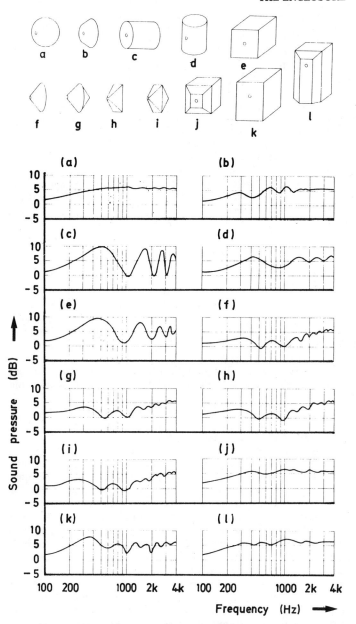

Figure 7.9   Twelve different enclosures tested for their effects on the final frequency response of a loudspeaker (after Olson)[8]

7.10 DRIVE-UNIT MOUNTING

The above considerations also concern the method of drive-unit mounting. For example, a 120 mm chassis mid-range unit should not be mounted behind a 12 mm to 18 mm panel if colouration due to diffraction and cavity resonance effects is to be avoided. Flush mounting in the front of the baffle is recommended for such drivers.

This suggestion may be ignored in the case of larger mid and bass-mid units as the front panel thickness is small relative to both the drive unit apertures and the sound wavelength produced.

A wooden block may be fitted to the cabinet to brace the magnet assembly of a driver possessing a weak pressed-steel chassis. This can reduce both driver and cabinet colouration. Recent work by KEF and B & W[9] has revealed that an appropriately compliant driver mounting gasket can usefully reduce cabinet resonances generated by energy transmission from the driver frame.

7.11 OPEN BAFFLES

Due to their simplicity, plane baffles were once the most common form encountered. For adequate bass the path length from the front to the rear of a given driver when baffled should be substantial, since it must be comparable with the wavelength of the lowest bass frequency required. A large baffle is a weak structure and thus prone to resonances unless it is well braced and loaded with sand or heavy bituminous pads.

As with enclosures, asymmetrical baffle shape and drive-unit mounting help to minimise cancellation and diffraction irregularities, and result in some low frequency extension.

A typical baffle area for adequate bass is 5 m^2, and with a suitable driver plus floor augmentation a 60 Hz cut off is possible at a reasonable pressure level.

Another problem with the simple baffle concerns the unwanted rear radiation, virtually equal to that from the front, the presence of which will affect both frequency balance and subjective colouration. This problem is also present with the other 'open-backed' systems such as the larger electrostatic and magnetically driven film-diaphragm speakers, as well as in units such as open ribbon-tweeters. However, the open baffle does have its advantages. While it is unwieldly in bass form, for mid and high frequency unit mounting it is free of the particular colouration produced by the alternative mid-range sub-enclosure. The sound of such a baffle is certainly 'open' and free of boxy effects, and several successful high performance systems have used reflex or sealed box bass sections in conjunction with smaller open baffle mid and upper mid components. Among these are the Bowers and Wilkins DM70, the Strathearn Audio speaker and the Dahlquist DQ10.

Against the advantage of subjectively perceived openness, must be weighed the unpredictable performance of such baffles in different locations, due to the rear radiation component. Another factor is the polar response, which differs markedly from a sealed enclosure and can cause design difficulties when the two are integrated at a crossover point. (See Section 2.1 on directivity.)

7.12 LOUDSPEAKER STANDS

A floor or wall mounted system will operate acoustically as if the adjacent surfaces are a continuation of the cabinet and, depending on the frequency radiated, acoustic coupling will occur between the two. The directivity theory indicates that at these lower frequencies (below 500 Hz) each adjacent surface will lift the apparent output by 3 dB.

If a system is balanced to give a natural sound in free space or semi-anechoic conditions it will be unbalanced by wall or floor mounting. A rigid open stand about 0.5 m high will transpose the range of lift due to local surfaces to a lower frequency to allow a reasonably accurate result from such a speaker, particularly in the critical region of the low mid-range.

It can thus be seen that the enclosure is by no means a simple box or baffle and that quite apart from considerations of low frequency driver loading (see Chapter 4) a number of other factors are also crucial in determining the subjective quality of the speaker system of which it forms an integral part.

REFERENCES

1. Stevens, W. R., 'Sound radiated from loudspeaker cabinets', *Proc. Audio Engng Soc. 50th Convention,* London, March (1975)
2. Beranek, L., *Noise and Vibration Control,* McGraw Hill
3. Barlow, D. A., 'Sound output of loudspeaker cabinet walls', *Proc. Audio Engng Soc. 50th Convention,* London, March (1975)
4. Fryer, P. A., 'Intermodulation distortion listening tests', *Proc. Audio Engng Soc. 50th Convention,* London, March (1975)
5. Harwood, H. D., 'Some factors in loudspeaker quality', *Wireless World,* 82, No.1485, p.45 et seq. (1976)
6. Terosow Werks GmbH., Heidelberg, Damping Material, British Patent 1 310 241
7. Payne, E. W., Wilson, P. I. and Wragg, W. T., 'Latest damping materials design out panel noise', *Design Engineering,* pp.54–57, May (1976)
8. Olsen, H. F., 'Direct radiator loudspeaker enclosures', *J. Audio Engng Soc.,* 17, No.1, 22–29 (1969)
9. Adams, G. J., 'New developments in L. S. Design – B & W 801', B & W Publication (1979)
10. Fincham, L. R., 'A bandpass loudspeaker enclosure', KEF Electronics Ltd (1979)

BIBLIOGRAPHY

Briggs, G. A., *Cabinet Handbook,* Wharfedale Wiresless Works, Idle, Yorkshire (1962)

Iverson, S. K., 'The theory of loudspeaker cabinet resonances', in 'Loudspeaker Anthology , *J. Audio Engng Soc.,* 1–25 (1979)

KEF Electronics Ltd., *You and Your Loudspeaker,* KEF Electronics Ltd., (c. 1970)

KEF Electronics Ltd., *Loudspeaker Testing Using Digital Techniques,* KEF Electronics Ltd., March (1975)

Tappan, P. W., 'Loudspeaker enclosure walls', in 'Loudspeaker Anthology', *J. Audio Engng Soc.,* 1–25 (1979)

Tremaine, H. M., *Audio Cyclopedia,* 2nd edn., Howard Sams, New York (1974)

8

Loudspeaker assessment

Evaluation is a fundamental part of the creation of any new product. In the case of a loudspeaker, although the subjective quality must be the ultimate arbiter of performance, subjective testing is arduous and fraught with difficulties. Figure 8.1 gives a suggested hierachy of the stages which may be involved in the complete evaluation of a loudspeaker system, this also including objective measurements.

Preceding chapters have outlined the technical aspects of loudspeaker engineering, and to a reader versed in the exact world of mechanical science, speaker technology might appear equally well defined. However, if this were the case, laboratory measurement alone would suffice to describe the entire performance of a speaker, including its sound quality. In fact, the present state of our knowledge is fairly limited as regards the significance of various distortions and their audibility thresholds, and despite much research into this aspect, subjective listening tests still represent a vital part of loudspeaker assessment. In themselves, such tests are a difficult proposition, for they involve psychoacoustic aspects of human perception, and due precautions need to be taken to ensure sufficiently reliable results.

This chapter covers all aspects of loudspeaker evaluation, both objective and subjective. An outline of the major parameters and distortions encountered with loudspeakers has been compiled, and where information is available, suggested standards and audibility thresholds are discussed.

8.1 LOUDSPEAKER SPECIFICATIONS, STANDARDS AND DISTORTIONS

Amplitude/frequency response

As with other items of equipment in the audio field, an adequately uniform response over the audible range is an obvious objective for the loudspeaker designer to aim at. Due to the strong interaction of the speaker's acoustic output with the listening environment, it is necessary to ask which response is the most important — total energy, the forward 2π hemisphere energy or the axial pressure, or perhaps something in-between[1,2]. Each philosophy has its proponents — for example, it has been proposed that for wall mounted systems, a flat energy response in the forward hemisphere produces the most natural sounding result. They are supported in this opinion by many of the Scandinavian manufacturers as well as by many European companies[3,4]. More specifically their aim is to produce an equal energy response over the frequency range in the listening room, this is obtained with systems designed for shelf mounting. However recent work conducted on the subjective quality and accuracy of commercial loudspeakers suggests that the most successful models have been designed virtually for free field use; and are best auditioned mounted on open stands as far away as is practicable from room walls or corners[5]. Such systems appear most natural if their anechoically measured axial response is essentially uniform with frequency, provided that certain other requirements are met, namely that the system should employ direct radiator drivers possessing a good directivity over the forward $\pm30°$ angle, and that the levels of distortion and delayed resonance colouration should be low[6,7]. This confirms BBC research findings and validates the basic historic standards for high quality loudspeakers, although it does assume that this type of speaker is fed with an accurately balanced programme which admittedly, is a relatively uncommon occurrence. As a result, modifications in the response uniformity may be required to suit different microphone techniques, for example.

Directivity

No worthwhile standard has been established for directivity — in other words, the uniformity of response over a defined forward radiating angle.   For a direct radiator system used for stereo, a predictably uniform output over the axial $60°$ solid angle is desirable, particularly in the lateral plane in order that a usefully wide stereo coverage is produced.

A suggested standard is 'deviation to be held within ±2 dB with respect to the axial curve over $\pm30°$ laterally, and $\pm10°$ vertically'. This would apply over the 100 Hz to 10 kHz range, 1/3 octave analysed, and should not be difficult to achieve using modern drive units. Outside of this angle, a rapid reduction in output may be considered a positive advantage, since the reflections from the adjacent walls would be diminished, with a consequent reduction in ambient energy and an improvement in stereo image stability.   However, in practice it is difficult to make the off-axis output independent of frequency.   An uncoloured speaker with a flat axial response but possessing an uneven off-axis characteristic, may nevertheless sound coloured in a listening room as the reverberant energy is derived from the total response, including that off-axis.

LOUDSPEAKER   APPRAISAL

A HEIRACHY OF MEASUREMENT, ANALYSIS, ASSESMENT AND JUDGMENT BOTH OBJECTIVE AND SUBJECTIVE.

TOTAL
APPRAISAL

OBJECTIVE MEASUREMENTS

IN SPECIALISED TEST ENVIRONMENTS

Listening room

a) ½ octave room response
b) Spl.
c) Real working sensitivity.

Reverberant room.

a) ½ octave energy response etc.
b) Absolute efficiency.

Anechoic or free field

a) Axial, off axis and polor frequency versus amplitude responses, steady state.
b) Harmonic and intermodulation distortion.
c) Doppler intermodulation.
d) Phase response.
e) Square wave or pulse response.
f) Toneburst response characteristics.
g) Axial sound pressure level for a known input power
h) Power handling capacity.

IN NON-CRITICAL TEST ENVIRONMENT

Measurement by signal gating some of the Anechoic tests are possible

Impulse response analysis by fast Fourier transform.

a) Frequency/amplitude response.
b) Impulse response.
c) Delayed responses.
d) Phase response.
e) Response synthesis.

Driver parameters.

a) Cone mass and area.
b) Cone damping.
c) Force factor
d) Etc.

General

a) Impedance Z.
b) Phase of impedance.
c) Resonant frequency.
d) DC resistance.

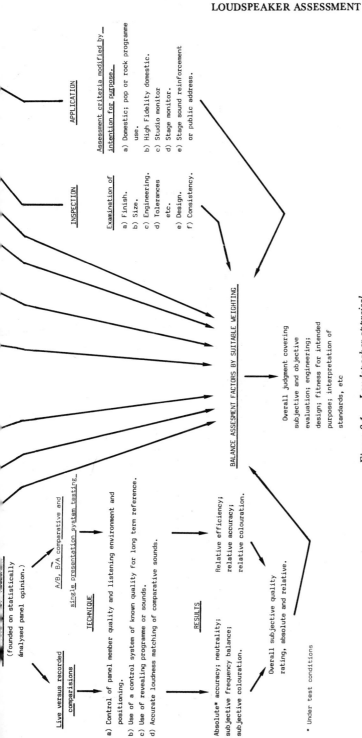

APPLICATION

Assessment criteria modified by intention for purpose.

a) Domestic; pop or rock programme use.
b) High Fidelity domestic.
c) Studio monitor.
d) Stage monitor.
e) Stage sound reinforcement or public address.

INSPECTION

Examination of

a) Finish.
b) Size.
c) Engineering.
d) Tolerances etc.
e) Design.
f) Consistency.

BALANCE ASSESMENT FACTORS BY SUITABLE WEIGHTING

Overall judgment covering subjective and objective evaluation; engineering; design; fitness for intended purpose; interpretation of standards, etc

(founded on statistically analysed panel opinion.)

Live versus recorded comparisions

A/B, B/A comparative and single presentation system testing

TECHNIQUE

a) Control of panel member quality and listening environment and positioning.
b) Use of a control system of known quality for long term reference.
c) Use of revealing programme or sounds.
d) Accurate loudness matching of comparative sounds.

RESULTS

Relative efficiency; relative accuracy; relative colouration.

Absolute* accuracy; neutrality; subjective frequency balance; subjective colouration.

Overall subjective quality rating, absolute and relative.

* Under test conditions

Figure 8.1   Loudspeaker appraisal

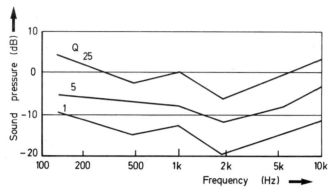

Figure 8.2   Detectability of resonances. 0 dB is a steady state level. At 2 kHz a 'Q' of 1 may be detected at a level 20 dB below the steady-state response, e.g. classical orchestral programme (after Fryer)[8]

Audibility of response irregularities

An investigation into the audibility of response irregularities has been conducted in England by P. A. Fryer of Rank-Leak-Wharfedale[8]. His tests have confirmed the long held suspicion that low Q deviations of small amplitude and broad extent can be considerably more significant than high Q narrow-band irregularities, mainly due to the reduced probability of exciting the latter. The results of this test may be relevant to steady state irregularities, since they concern the addition of resonant components whose peak amplitude could be less than the reference level, but which nevertheless produced mild humps in the total response. The ear's sensitivity to such resonances was higher for pink noise than for popular music, with a classical orchestral programme falling somewhere in between.   Figure 8.2 shows that by using the latter type of material, resonant 'Qs' = 25 or more could be of similar amplitude to the steady state before being detected, whereas 'Qs' = 1 which might be expected to be less audible in fact are more noticeable. At 2.5 kHz, the region of peak sensitivity, the panel noted the effect of a resonance of $Q = 1$, at a level full 20 dB below the steady state response. The ear's high sensivity to broad acting, low amplitude response irregularities, (approximately 1 dB) will be examined at a later point in this chapter.

Harwood has stated that certain other features of frequency response are responsible for obvious subjective effects, notably the presence of a series in a sequence of irregularities. If these are random, they seem to be relatively innocuous, but if regular, the ear appears to assign strong colouration to them, even if it can be proven that the level of the delayed resonances is otherwise insignificant. The location of a speaker system in a room can invoke such a series of resonances, which are subjectively as obvious as those which can occur in the system itself. A further investigation concerned the audibility of irregularities, with peaks and dips of magnitude ±3 dB. If these were more closely spaced than 1/3 octave, and were not present in the form of a regular series, then they proved inaudible under programme conditions[10].

It is evident that on a subjective basis broad deviations in response are more obvious to a listener and that perhaps weighted on an octave band basis, the speaker designer should be aiming for a deviation of ±0.25 dB or less in the forward directed response, while according rather less importance to narrow band deviations of greater amplitude which hitherto may have occupied his attention.

Further confirmation of this 'averaged response' criterion was provided by a recent panel test which involved the assessment of thirty pairs of commercial loudspeakers[5]. The identities of the speakers were concealed from the panel, and the systems auditioned included both small models with good bass transient performance but necessarily limited bandwidths, and considerably larger systems, with a wider bandwidth but a generally poorer bass transient response.

The panel invariably voiced a preference for the smaller models, providing that they were not overloaded. In fact, even a miniature loudspeaker of 8 litres volume was found capable of sounding natural in a 'full' and 'spacious' manner — more so in fact than many of the larger systems to which this quality is more likely to be attributed. Subsequent analysis revealed that the favoured speakers were those which possessed very even axial responses over 100 Hz to 10 kHz when measured by third octave and octave averaging.

Mid-band uniformity and overall spectral balance would thus appear to be a crucial area of speaker performance.

Nonlinear distortion

Except for gross effects induced by overload or a mechanical failure, there is little evidence to suggest that the distortions measured in electronics such as amplifiers are of the same subjective nature as those perceived with loudspeakers[10,11]. While levels of below 0.1% for harmonic and intermodulation distortion are well worth attaining with an amplifier, providing that the transient characteristics are not compromised, higher levels of loudspeaker distortion appear to be of less consequence.

As little correlation appears to exist between subjective sound quality and distortion characteristics in speakers, their interpretation is somewhat arbitrary. Moir compiled a graph of lower limit detectability of harmonic distortion on single tones (Fig.8.3) which shows that below 400 Hz, distortion greater than 1% on second and third harmonics is undetectable. At 60 Hz, over 7.5% of third harmonic content is inaudible, and likewise at 80 Hz, over 40% of second harmonic content lies below the audibility threshold.

At frequencies higher than 400 Hz there is little evidence to indicate that harmonic distortion above 1% is audible. For example, the Din standard 45,500 which is applicable to hi fi systems states that for

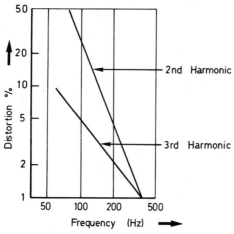

Figure 8.3 '*Just detectable' harmonic distortion on single tones (after Moir)*[14,15]

96 dB s.p.l. at 1 m, the distortion should be less than 3% total harmonic from 250 Hz to 1 kHz, reducing to less than 1% above 2 kHz, this range extending to 5 kHz.

Fryer examined the sensitivity of a small but representative panel to first order $(f_1 + f_2, f_2 - f_1)$ intermodulation distortion* reproduced by loudspeakers, this distortion generated electrically to a high standard of accuracy. The test programme included popular, classical orchestral and solo piano material. Overall, the threshold of detectability of intermodulation distortion lay at the 4 to 5% level. Experienced listeners demonstrated a 2 to 4% threshold on piano, and unskilled female panellists a similar sensitivity on pop music. On pure tones the results were dependent on the level of the fundamental which was controlled by room resonance effects. Distortion thresholds of about 1% are indicated for pure tone tests[7]. Interestingly enough, neither sound pressure level (within reasonable limits) or loudspeaker type (from large four-way systems to small two-way bookcase models) had any detectable influence on these results. This finding suggests that the residual intermodulation distortion of the test reproducers were negligible. The conditions for this experiment were related to a domestic situation, with the programme derived from disc, which will inevitably contain both considerable intermodulation and harmonic distortion. The music thresholds might have well been closer to the pure tone levels had higher quality programme such as master tapes been employed.

MacKenzie suggests that a maximum of 0.25% harmonic and intermodulation content for the 'mid-range' (200 Hz to 7 kHz) is a desirable limit, and his recent report on loudspeakers indicates that in the absence

* Fundamental frequencies (f_1, f_2). The 1st order distortion products are the sum and difference frequencies of the fundamentals

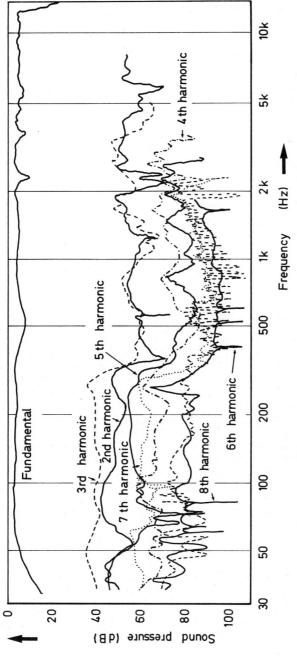

Figure 8.4   Harmonic distortion of LS5/5 loudspeaker measured at 1 N/m² at 1.5 m (after Harwood)⁶

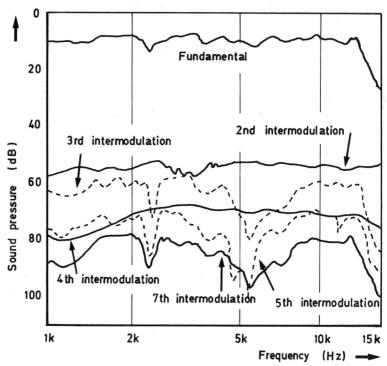

*Figure 8.5   Intermodulation distortion of LS5/5 loudspeaker measured at 1 N/m²
at 1.5 m (after Harwood)*[6]

of other masking effects, subjective quality degradation is present with
systems containing levels of over 1% in the 700 Hz to 12 kHz band. His
test method utilised a 300 Hz difference frequency, measuring the upper
third product $(2f_1 - f_2)$ from 400 Hz to 20 kHz, with f_1 tracking below[13].
However, the first order intermodulation product may not represent
the entire solution to the problem, and higher orders are well worth
investigating. For example, BBC designs are examined during development for harmonic distortion to the 8th, and intermodulation products
to the 7th order (Figs.8.4 and 8.5)[6].

Smoothly changing distortion curves are considered favourable while
the presence of sharp discontinuities indicates breakup modes with
other serious consequences in terms of irregular directivity and impaired
transient performance. If there are any doubts that low distortion is
possible from a loudspeaker, the curves for the Yamaha NS1000 should
dispel them (Fig.8.6).

This model, a three-way sealed box system using a 300 mm pulp
cone bass, an 88 mm dome mid and 30 mm treble unit, was tested

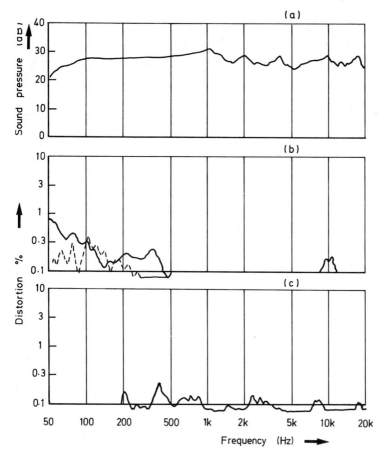

Figure 8.6 A low distortion speaker system by Yamaha, at 90 dB lin approximately, at 1 m. (a) Axial presure response, (b) 2nd and 3rd harmonics and (c) intermodulation $(2f_1 - f_2)$ product where $f_2 - f_1 = 300$ Hz. (After MacKenzie)[13]

at a 90 dB reference level at 1 m. Above 500 Hz the second and third harmonics were typically below 0.1%, and the intermodulation product over the same range in general measured 0.15%. To illustrate rather more typical distortion results, the response graph of an American three-way system taken under the same conditions is included for comparison (Fig.8.7).

Frequency-modulation distortion

This is often described as 'Doppler distortion', but more correctly it

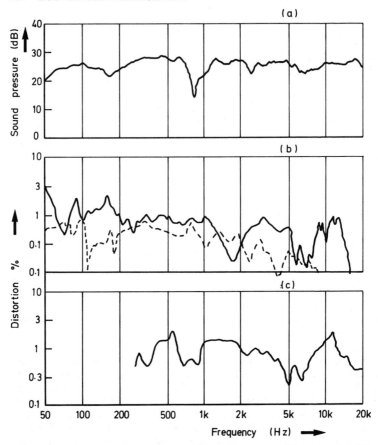

*Figure 8.7   Typical distortion results; (a) axial pressure, (b) 2nd and 3rd har-
monics and (c) $2f_1 - f_2$ intermodulation product. 90 dB at 1 m, $2f_1 - f_2 = 300$
Hx.) (After MacKenzie)*[13]

refers to a series of distortion harmonics produced when the frequency
of one signal is modulated by another.* This occurs when a drive unit
diaphragm or even a local reflecting surface radiating a high frequency
is simultaneously radiating another lower frequency, where a greater
excursion occurs. A typical example would be as a bass driver reproducing low and mid-range signals.

* The figures for Doppler distortion are described in two different forms, either
as a percentage of frequency shift of the upper frequency, this figure thus constant with respect to the latter, or alternatively as a percentage of the Doppler
introduced harmonic sidebands relative to the amplitude of the unshifted upper
signal. This second method gives a figure which is proportional to the upper
signal frequency and thus varies considerably over the spectrum.

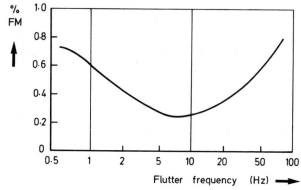

Figure 8.8   Subjective thresholds for piano music, frequency modulated by a pure 'flutter' frequency (after Stott and Axon)[16]

One may speculate about the importance of minimising FM distortion, since a microphone transducing a wide-range programme at high sound intensities will possess FM components in its output. The bass frequencies will cause the diaphragm to move while simultaneously receiving the higher notes. Could a loudspeaker impart some cancellation of this distortion when reproducing such programme? A brief examination of the amplitude of microphone diaphragm motion at typical sound pressure levels shows that such frequency modulation is in fact negligible, and hence such cancellation will not occur.

Several authorities have discussed the problem of FM distortion, and some have suggested that the audibility thresholds are very low; Moir[14,15] has shown that 0.002% is detectable when using a modulating frequency of 20 Hz and a pure tone fundamental. Further work, in this instance using music programme and a revised sensitivity threshold, has suggested that 0.1% might be the level detectable by the experienced listener. A particularly relevant investigation of that conducted by Scott and Axon[16], concerning the high frequency pitch variations classed as flutter, which are also a form of FM distortion. Thresholds of about 1% were determined (Fig.8.8).

In this light, Moir's more recent threshold of 0.1% might appear to be a possible objective to match future equipment and programme standards.

For a given type of diaphragm however, it would seem that while FM distortion reduces with increasing cone size and consequently reduced LF excursions, the non-linear amplitude modulation distortions, namely harmonic and intermodulation, remain independent of cone size. With large units, for example, of 300 mm diameter, the FM and AM distortions are almost equal at the 1% level, (at 85 dB s.p.l.) while for the 100 mm diameter size, the distortion is likely to be dominated by FM components 14 dB greater in level.

However the ration of FM to AM components depends strongly on the type of driver. Klipsh[17] was unfortunate enough to measure a rather poor 200 mm mid-range unit (judged from the reproduced frequency response) which produced up to 15% total harmonic and intermodulation distortion within its working band (540 Hz and 4400 Hz, f_1, f_2 when producing 100 dB at 0.62 m). Such a performance is not, in my opinion, representative of current high performance examples. He also investigated a full range compact multiple driver system which was designed for use with an equaliser, and found that at $f_1 = 50$ Hz, $f_2 = 750$ Hz, both set to 95 dB s.p.l. at 0.62 m, the AM content was 14% as compared with the FM content of 3%.

A relevant point in this context is that significant FM distortion is only produced under high LF excursion which does not occur very often with the average programme.

Judged on subjective grounds FM distortion in general does not appear to be a major effect. The consumer tests[5] demonstrated that on wide range programme played at a reasonable level (85 dB average in a fair sized room, measured at 2 m), a very high quality 8 litre two-way sealed box system subjectively outperformed a number of full size three-way systems, of 50–100 litres volume. The small enclosure involved was based on a BBC design and designated LS3/5a. If any system should have failed because of unacceptably high FM content, this would have been the one since at this volume level the harmonic distortion was under 1% and hence could not provide masking.

Recently published research conducted by Rank-Leak-Wharfedale[9] indicates that the maximum allowable excursion to be 0.4 cm peak, for a wide range driver, before FM distortion becomes audible. Their test method employed electronically simulated Doppler distortion through the use of a variable delay line. The miniature system described above just meets this criterion at the level used for the consumer test, as in fact do most other quality speakers used within their intended loudness range. Clearly for normal sized systems, FM distortion cannot be subjectively significant, regardless of its proven existence, even at realistic listening levels.

Transient response and colouration
Speech and music are largely asymmetric in waveform structure, and theoretically they demand an accurate pulse or transient response from the loudspeaker. If the standards often applied to the other components in the audio chain were applied to loudspeakers, then the acoustic output of a loudspeaker would decay to negligible levels 0.025 ms after the cessation of a narrow impulse excitation.

Viewed in a pessimistic light, a loudspeaker may be regarded as an assembly of more or less well damped resonances spaced across the audible frequency range, and it thus has little hope of meeting such a requirement. Fortunately the human ear's inherent discrimination of transients is poorer than the above mentioned standard, and there are indications that a decay rate of 10 dB per millisecond immediately after the excitation is a realistic level to aim for, with the rate decreasing exponentially after the first 20 or 30 dB decay.

The energy hangover after the impulse has passed is similar to reverberation, and in some speaker designs it has been deliberately encouraged to provide a falsely weighty and spacious subjective effect. Since such a hangover is strongly frequency dependent, 'delayed resonance' is a more appropriate term, and in practice subjective colouration associated with its presence may be ascribed to the frequencies at which it occurs.

Some speaker designers believe that a transient response of the same characteristic as a quality amplifier is necessary from a loudspeaker and have exhaustively pursued aspects such as truthful square wave reproduction. Such a performance by definition requires that the amplitude versus frequency response be sensibly flat; that the overshoot or ringing at any frequency be minimal, and that no differential time delay or frequency unrelated phase shift is present between sections of the audible spectrum. It has been suggested that a speaker with differential time delays, that is, a non-minimum phase characteristic, must sound coloured in this respect, although there is still a matter of dispute.

Colouration remains a major fault with loudspeakers, where the main problem concerns its subjectivity. One listener may prefer a certain system to another solely on the basis of differing colouration, whilst neither may in fact be superior. Colouration can certainly be attributed to delayed resonances whose effects may be imperceptible in terms of an irregularity on the steady state frequency response, but whose presence is plainly visible on a frequency analysis taken a millisecond or longer after an impulse excitation, and may be equally obvious on subjective grounds (Fig.8.9).

Delayed resonances are a major cause of colouration and can result from many effects such as unwanted vibration in cabinet walls, drive unit resonances and inadequately damped electrical resonances in the crossover network. Visible broad-band unevenness in the frequency response curve will also result in subjectively perceived colouration (see Table 8.5).

Phase

There has been a resurgence of interest in the general audibility of phase effects and in particular, their relationship to the design of loudspeakers. The measurement of phase was rather difficult until the introduction of modern digital delay-lines, and certain manufactures, notably Technics, Bang and Olufsen, Bowers and Wilkins, have since produced linear or more correctly 'minimum phase' loudspeaker systems. The Quad Electrostatic speaker also belongs to this group, although at the time of its introduction in 1955, the aspect of minimum phase was not accorded much importance.

Recently a number of papers and articles have been published on this controversial subject[18–27] and although the author does not intend to commit himself, clearly some review of the matter is in order. It has yet to be demonstrated that minimum phase speaker designs are sub-

(a) Impulse response

(b)(c) Frequency response
(at t = 0, i.e. steady state)

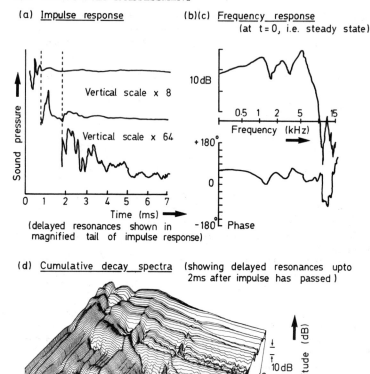

(d) Cumulative decay spectra (showing delayed resonances upto 2ms after impulse has passed)

Figure 8.9   110 mm moving-coil bass/mid-range unit in a 7 litre closed box. (a) Impulse response, (b) and (c) frequency response (at t = 0, i.e. steady state equivalent), (d) cumulative delay spectra (showing delayed resonances up to 2 ms after impulse has passed). (Courtesy KEF Electronics Ltd)

jectively more accurate on programme signals than other high quality but conventional systems; in fact, 'linear phase' speakers to date have generally not attained the same standard set by conventional high quality monitors. The limitations imposed by minimum phase techniques appear to be partially responsible, and whatever benefits 'linear phase' offers, they are clearly insufficient at present to make up the quality deficit. Nevertheless there are strong indications that minimum phase designs do offer improved stereo imaging and greater apparent depth, particularly when auditioned using coherent stereo programme, and the technique cannot be dismissed out of hand (see Fig. 6.2, also Appendix 3).

Impedance (as seen by an amplifier at the loudspeaker terminals)

At first sight one might not expect the input impedance characteristic of a loudspeaker to have much influence over the reproduced sound quality, but in practice problems can occur when an amplifier is connected to a speaker system.

With some loudspeakers containing complex crossovers, the designer may have sacrificed the uniformity of impedance to optimise other characteristics, such as axial response. Only the finest amplifiers are able to drive difficult loads without some subjective quality deterioration, and even with these, the maximum output is inevitably reduced. Poor quality amplifiers can thus produce quite disappointing results with loudspeaker systems possessing a demanding reactive impedance characteristic.

A suggested standard which will give good results with the present generation of power amplifiers is for a complex impedance of $Z = 8\ \Omega$, ±20% with a phase angle not exceeding ±30° over the range, 100 Hz to 10 kHz.

Non-standard impedances are troublesome on several counts. For example, they make it difficult to specify true sensitivity, because the nominal power delivery of the matching amplifier is indeterminate. Take the example of a system where the designer aimed to make a speaker 'apparently' more efficient with a standard 8 Ω based amplifier. Instead of increasing magnet flux, this was achieved by reducing the system impedance to an average of 5.5 Ω, from a nominal 8 Ω. At moderate levels where the amplifier was unstressed, the extra power required was delivered with a consequent sensitivity improvement, but towards full power the situation was reversed. The low impedance induced premature amplifier clipping of an unpleasant nature, and ultimately, the maximum tolerable sound pressure level produced by the combination was less than that for the original 8 Ω based design. The practice of specifying voltage sensitivity may gain acceptance, and is quite sensible in view of the low output impedance of modern amplifiers.

8.2 MEASUREMENT AND EVALUATION: INTRODUCTION

From an engineering viewpoint, loudspeaker assessment might appear fairly straightforward: drive units can be specified to a sufficient degree to guarantee a predictable measured standard. However in practice, objective measurement alone is insufficient to fully describe the sound quality, and subjective evaluation is also essential, with the loudspeaker system preferably judged through reference to live sound.

Subjective appraisal is the final arbiter in the judgment of quality. While engineering theory and mathematics will provide the foundation for a design whose technical accuracy and soundness may be verified by objective measurement, until a valid listening test is undertaken the true merit of the design cannot be assessed.

The total evaluation of a loudspeaker is thus a complex and wide ranging operation whose basic content is outlined in Fig.8.1 under 'Loudspeaker Appraisal'. The two sections, namely objective and subjective assessment, are dealt with separately, in this section and in section 8.4.

Objective or instrument based measurements

Figure 8.1 covers the bulk of the useful tests which may concern complete loudspeaker systems or individual drivers, when suitably mounted on a panel or baffle.

Test environment

Most loudspeaker measurements utilise a precision microphone to pick up the sound pressure from the test loudspeaker. The test environment is of considerable importance, as the readings may be strongly affected by sound reflections under normal reverberant conditions.

For those where such interference must be eliminated, the speaker should be taken to a 'free-field' or open-air location and elevated clear of the ground. Cooke[28] indicates that an 8 m elevation is sufficient for a 1 m microphone-to-loudspeaker spacing, provided that the speaker is mounted front uppermost with the microphone positioned above it, in order to minimise reflections. If atmospheric conditions are favourable, this true free-field location gives more accurate results than an artificial echoless environment, usually an anechoic chamber (Fig.8.10).

In such a chamber, of moderate size, the optimum working range is limited to 200 Hz to 10 kHz, with a typical absorption of 90% of the sound energy, though with careful calibration the low frequency range may be extended to 50 Hz (near field).

The inconvenience of outdoor measurements where ambient noise (passing aircraft and cars, etc.) is a nuisance, means that anechoic chambers are widely employed. Provided that their imperfections are understood and noted, they are invaluable for loudspeaker measurement. Typical anechoic chambers consist of an acoustically isolated room of massive brick or concrete construction, lined internally with wedges of polyurethane foam or fibreglass up to a metre in length. Good absorption of sound is offered down to wavelengths comparable with twice the wedge depth, typically 200 Hz. Below this, the low frequency absorption becomes less effective, and the characteristic of the anechoic chamber gradually reverts to a free field pressure chamber much like an ordinary room of similar dimensions. A further difficulty encountered with free field measurement is the necessity for the microphone to be

Figure 8.10   Anechoic chamber (courtesy Acoustic Research)

in the far-field; that is, several wavelengths distant at the lowest frequency in the range covered. Clearly low frequencies will present the most problems. The microphone must also be positioned at a greater distance from the test system than the largest panel dimension, to avoid near-field diffraction. At 30 Hz the required separation of microphone and system makes any kind of free-field measurement almost impossible; either the chambers are not large enough or the signal-to-ambient-noise ratio in open air is likely to be inadequate.

At the normal 1 m microphone spacing, with the tests conducted in an average chamber, the low frequency section of a curve at typically below 150 Hz will begin to approximate to a pressure response, with the microphone located in the low frequency near-field. It is fortunate that for domestic speaker applications, the dimensions of the listening room are not too dissimilar from those of the anechoic chamber. Hence both possess a similar broad averaged pressure response and the measurements taken in the chamber still make practical sense. This is however only valid for moderate room sizes, and acoustic conditions will be entirely different if a loudspeaker is used in a large hall, where the free-field response radiation will continue down to a correspondingly lower frequency.

Recently developed methods for response measurements using pulse signals, where the test room reflections and ambient noise may be suppressed by suitable synchronised gating, can offer some improvement, but the theoretical necessity to remove the microphone to the far field still remains.

2π- and 4π-environments

There are several philosophies concerning test environments. Some manufacturers, typified by Acoustic Research, generally design their systems for domestic wall mounted use, radiating into a hemispherical or 2π-space. Thus when measuring their own systems, Acoustic Research often employ a 2π-anechoic chamber, where one wall is reflecting and carries the test system flush mounted, the suggestions being that this test condition corresponds most closely to normal domestic useage.

Another philosophy whose main exponents are the Scandinavian and other European Companies, requires that a loudspeaker deliver a nearly flat energy response. For such a system a totally reflecting reverberant chamber is employed, which allows a summation of the total energy output to be made via the averaging of the output from a microphone (Fig.8.11).

A further philosophy and one to which the Author personally subscribes, is that axial pressure responses taken in nominally free-field anechoic conditions at a normal listening distance (2 m), are the most relevant to the subjectively perceived sound quality of a system. This is provided that such a system is used in a domestic situation which approximates to those conditions prevailing in the anechoic chamber — that is, elevated from the floor on an open stand and clear of adjacent walls by at least half a metre. Most of the international standards on loudspeaker measurement relate to these conventional anechoic arrangements (microphone distance 1 or 2 m), and hence it will be accorded appropriate importance in the succeeding sections.

8.3 OBJECTIVE MEASUREMENTS

Amplitude/frequency responses (4π or full anechoic)

Sine excitation

A number of tests may be performed with sinewave excitation derived from a power amplifier fed by a suitable automatic sweep-oscillator system. The usual input level is a nominal 1 W referred to 8 Ω

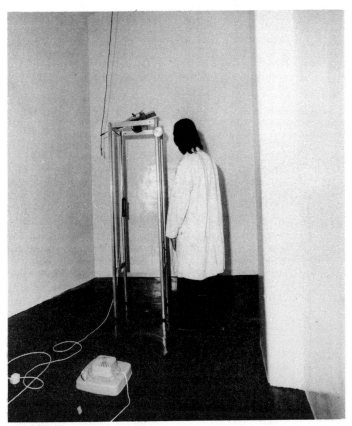

Figure 8.11   Reverberant chamber (courtesy Acoustic Research). Note the hard surfaces, asymmetrical geometry, humidifier (on the floor) and the microphone with motorised rotator (on the stand). The test system is flush-mounted in the wall behind the camera

(2.83 V r.m.s.) with the microphone (generally a 12.5 mm capsule) placed at 1 or 2 m from the mid- or treble-drivers.

Figure 8.12 is virtually self-explanatory and shows the test arrangement using typical equipment. The trace obtained (Fig.8.13) is a widely used specification for loudspeakers, and with certain reservations is probably the most important. The 2π low frequency response alone may be accurately quantified via a close proximity ($<$5 cm) microphone position, this valid in the piston range[32]. (See Section 8.4, et seq on subjective assessment.)

Clearly only direct radiating systems with forward facing drivers on a plane or nearly plane driver panel can be accurately quantified by this

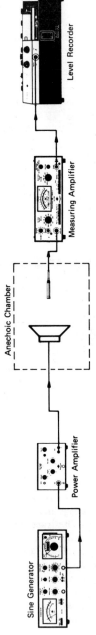

Figure 8.12 Set-up for acoustical frequency response measurements (courtesy Bruel & Kjaer)[31]

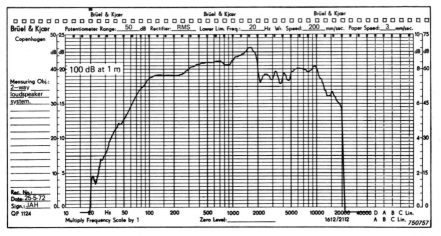

Figure 8.13   Sine response curve of a medium quality two-way loudspeaker system (courtesy Bruel & Kjaer)[31]

method. The appearance of a sine wave response trace may be influenced by test conditions; for example, the pen speed on the chart recorder. An exceptionally slow pen speed will tend to smooth sharp resonances or dips, thus giving a false impression of the speaker.

With multi-unit systems, interference dips may exist at specific microphone positions, and a lateral or vertical displacement of a few centimetres or so, can result in this dip disappearing, or another appearing. For these reasons, great care is required in the interpretation of sine wave responses and an initial curve may need confirmation by further tests taken at slightly different microphone positions.

The curve illustrated in Fig.8.13 has the instrument settings recorded on it for future reference, those shown being typical of modern measurement techniques.

Off-axis responses

These are typically $\pm 10°$ or $\pm 15°$ in the vertical plane and $\pm 20°$ or $\pm 30°$ in the lateral plane. Both sine and noise excitation is common. In addition to the axial response measurement, the loudspeaker may be angled or rotated to allow polar plots at single frequencies off-axis. These plots often reveal irregularities not shown on-axis, for example, if a unit's dispersion narrows, or the energy at the crossover point between two drivers is not integrating properly due to phase differences. Such a dip might not be apparent on a single axial response measurement as a result of fortunate microphone placement (see Figs.7.8 and 8.14).

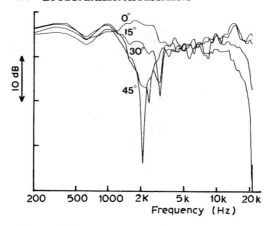

Figure 8.14   Family of oblique frequency response curves at 0°, 15°, 30° and 45°, 1 m in horizontal plane. (Courtesy KEF Electronics Ltd)

Random noise excitation

Whilst a sine test signal is potentially the most accurate and precise, random noise is also valuable for loudspeaker measurement. There is strong evidence that the ear tends to average short-term irregularities and is rather more sensitive to broader trends in energy over third-octave or octave bandwidths.

Third-octave or octave bandwidth analysed noise provides a convenient method for such averaging. From a philosophical point of view, noise more closely resembles music programme in transient content than sine wave, and hence could be considered more relevant. It also readily permits the measurement of the 'A'* weighted or subjective based loudness of the system. If broadband noise is applied to the loudspeaker, the filtered analysis of the total output provides some ambient noise suppression due to the narrow detector bandwidth. Alternatively the drive to the speaker may be pre-filtered and the microphone amplifier left in the wide-band condition (Figs.8.15 and 18.16).

Gated sine wave excitation

Bruel and Kjaer have produced an instrument for gating the output of a signal generator[29] which simultaneously samples and stores the peak amplitude of the received output long enough for a continuous response trace to be recorded (Fig.8.17).

Through the elimination of local wall reflections, the need for an

* 'A' weighting is a measurement response tailored to match the subjective loudness characteristic of the ear

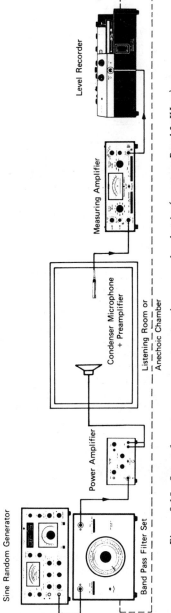

Figure 8.15   Set-up for response measurements using narrow band noise (courtesy Bruel & Kjaer)

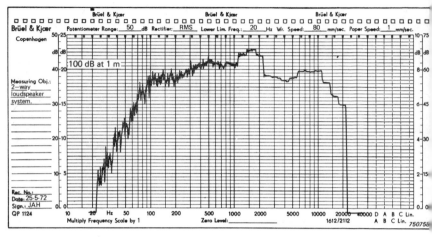

Figure 8.16 *Some techniques vary the writing speed during the sweep in order to give the analysis records a more uniform appearance, usually from 10 mm/s at 20 Hz to 160 mm/s at 2 kHz and above. This trace shows a 1/3 octave analysis without such adjustment. (Courtesy Bruel & Kjaer)*

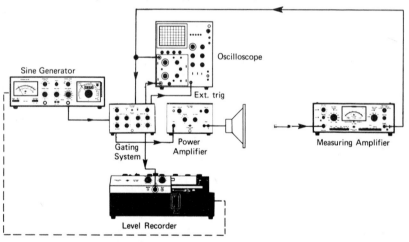

Figure 8.17 *Set-up using gating system. (Courtesy Bruel & Kjaer)*

anechoic environment is removed, and measurements may be performed at mid and high frequencies in an ordinary reflective room (Fig.8.18). In reasonably open conditions frequency/amplitude response measurements of fair accuracy can be made with noise or 1/3 octave warbled sine wave excitation which suppresses local reflected modes. Depending on the nearest surface, typically 100 Hz upwards measurement is feasible.

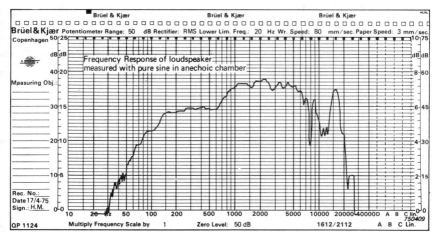

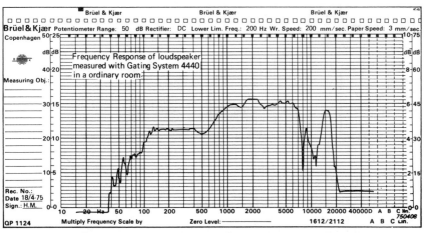

Figure 8.18 Frequency response of loudspeaker measured in anechoic chamber and frequency response of same loudspeaker measured with gating system. (Courtesy Bruel & Kjaer)

Impulse excitation

The use of a digital computer equipped with a fast Fourier transform processor allows full analysis of the pulse response of a loudspeaker. A pulse-gating technique similar to that described above is employed, providing suppression of room reflections. From the pulse analysis the steady state response may be derived automatically and plotted in the usual way (Fig.8.19). Figures 8.20 and 8.21 show the responses of the same loudspeaker derived by steady-state sine wave, and by pulse analysis[30].

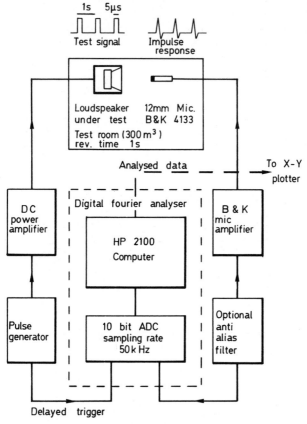

Figure 8.19   Lay-out for loudspeaker impulse measurements (after KEF Electronics)

Other systems for gated analysis also allow the investigation of delayed resonances and reflections through the analysis of the output of a system after the initial excitation is over. For example, the arrangement in Fig.8.17, if used with an anechoic chamber to suppress the room reflections, may be adjusted so that the gating control unit reads the output after cessation of the burst excitation.

Microprocessor developments have enabled the production of relatively low cost F.F.T. analysers such as the HP3582A which may be set up with a pulse generator to produce an effective impulse test system Fig.8.22(a). The required analyser time window may be adjusted to examine the portion of the loudspeaker impulse response of interest via a signal gate, Fig.8.22(b).

An indication of the importance of impulse testing is given by the

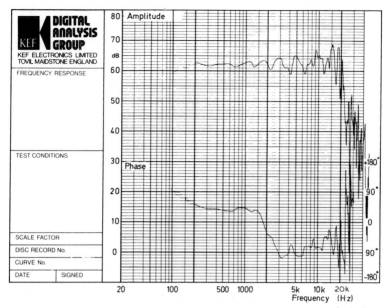

Figure 8.20 Axial pressure response via computer analysis of pulse response

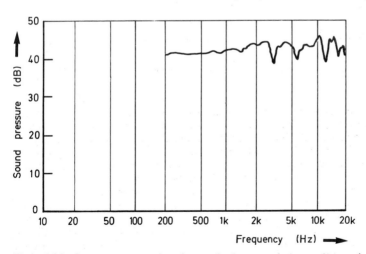

Figure 8.21 System response by sine excitation: anechoic conditions (same model as in Fig.8.20)

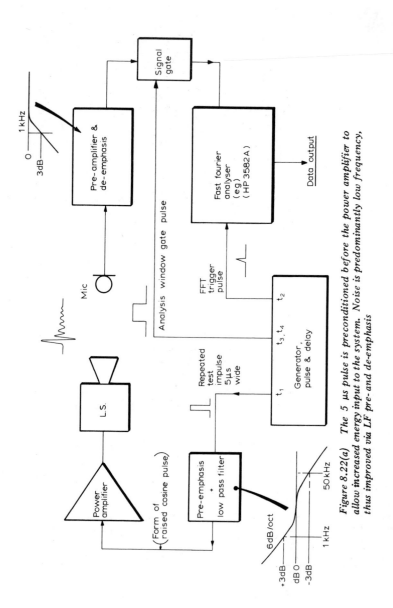

Figure 8.22(a)   The 5 μs pulse is preconditioned before the power amplifier to allow increased energy input to the system. Noise is predominantly low frequency, thus improved via LF pre- and de-emphasis

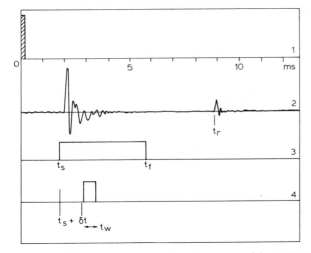

Figure 8.22(b)   Impulse response and capture.   (1) Applied impulse typically 5 μs wide.   (2) Impulse response of loudspeaker in ordinary room with first wall reflection at t_r.   Delay t_s due to propagation from microphone to speaker, over approximately 1 m.   (3) t_s to t_f defines the time window for the analyser to capture the entire pulse response.   (4) A signal gate window $t_w \simeq 0.5$ ms at δt after t_s allows analysis of the delayed resonance energy remaining after the main impulse is over

costly investment carried out by many companies in acquiring the necessary measuring equipment.   The Rank/Wharfedale research team has also achieved success in delayed resonance analysis, their 'in-house' system (Fig.8.23 and 8.24) developed by using a variation of the gated tone-burst set-up described earlier with burst length proportional to frequency for constant excitation over the frequency range.   The output appears in conventional log frequency format from 20 Hz to 20 kHz.[34] The essential features of this method were in fact first established by Shorter at the BBC as early as 1945.

Harmonic and intermodulation distortion

Distortion can vary dramatically over quite a small frequency interval, and for this reason, continuous distortion versus frequency sweeps are usually taken.

The basic set-up for distortion measurement is similar to the amplitude/frequency response arrangement (Fig.8.25), with the addition of a suitable selective analyser or tracking filter interposed between recorder and microphone.   The filter may be offset or displaced by a suitable harmonic interval so that any order of harmonic may be recorded.   The

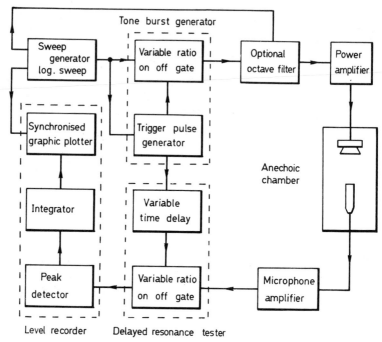

Figure 8.23   Delayed resonance testing (after Fryer)[9]

use of a two-tone generator with a tracking harmonic multiplier also allows swept intermodulation traces to be recorded.

Figures 8.6 and 8.7 shows two such curves. The $2f_2 - f_1$ 2nd order intermodulation product was traced with $f_1 - f_2 = 300$ Hz, and the combined tone level was set at 90 dB at 1 m. These swept intermodulation measurements may well prove more revealing than the usual single harmonic readings.

One self-evident point is the relationship between sound level and distortion, the latter usually increasing with the former. It is thus sensible to choose a standard level for comparative purposes, e.g. 90 dB. The Din standard specified 96 dB, which is on the high side for most low colouration HF units on continuous tone. The suggested lower level applies to domestic and low level monitor systems, and would not be adequate for high level monitor or large audience broadcast arrays, where 100 to 120 dB at 1 m would be a more relevant test sound pressure.

Doppler distortion

The measurement of Doppler distortion is not easy, as the FM components must be separated from the other accompanying distortions, and this tends to restrict the range of measurements (Fig.8.26).

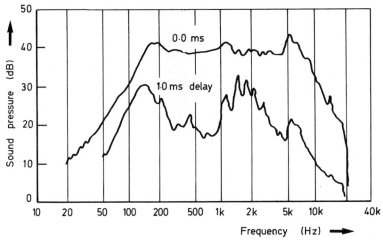

Figure 8.24 The upper curve shows the normal steady state response of what appears from this curve to be a good mid-range unit. Listening tests however show this is not the case and the lower delayed response curve indicates why. The hump in the curve at around 2 kHz badly colours the sound of this speaker and yet it hardly affects the steady state response at all (after Fryer)[9]

Noise intermodulation distortion

Intermodulation distortion may be measured using a random noise signal. The same arrangement as that employed for third-octave analysis is followed (Fig.8.16), but with the addition of another, tracking third-octave filters. One operates on the noise source and the other filters the microphone output signal. With the latter shifted a harmonic interval above the input or fundamental third octave, various combined harmonic/intermodulation curves may be obtained over third-octave bandwidths.

Phase response

The recent introduction of a high quality delay line (e.g. Bruel and Kjaer 6202) facilitates the steady state measurement of the phase response versus frequency of a loudspeaker (Fig.8.27).

The phase characteristic may also be derived via F.F.T. analysis of the impulse response (see Fig.8.20).

Minimum phase

Several manufacturers have recently introduced 'linear phase' loudspeakers. In fact, the correct term to describe such systems is 'mini-

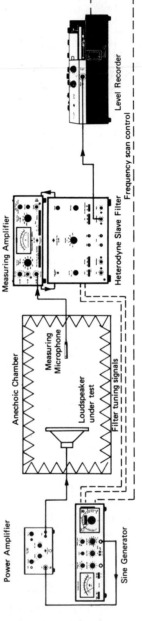

Figure 8.25   Total harmonic distortion measurement (courtesy Bruel & Kjaer)

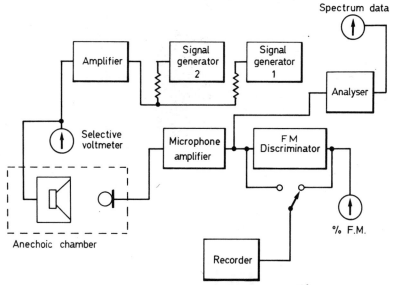

Figure 8.26   Doppler distortion measurement set-up (after Moir)[14]

mum phase', which implies that a well defined linear relationship exists between the amplitude and phase response of the speaker; that is, the phase varies linearly with frequency (note that the phase does not have to be constant with frequency*). In a multi-unit system, the drivers are usually mounted on a flat baffle or front panel, with their effective radiation planes displaced by varying degrees depending on chassis geometry diaphragm type and panel depth, etc. In such a case a relative time delay will exist between the outputs of the different drive units. measured at the listening position this producing a non-minimum phase characteristic. Using the phase measuring apparatus, these time delays may be quantified and the units may then be aligned so that this differential delay is substantially minimised, thus allowing minimum phase system design, assuming a suitable crossover is utilised.

Square wave and impulse response

A loudspeaker must have a perfect amplitude and phase response to reproduce a square wave with its complex related harmonic structure. However, only minimum phase loudspeakers are potentially able to do this with any degree of accuracy, and other designs will give practically meaningless results on this test.

The impulse response is another matter, as the aim of this measurement is to evaluate delayed resonances in the crossover, the driver

* This is implicit in the term 'linear phase'.

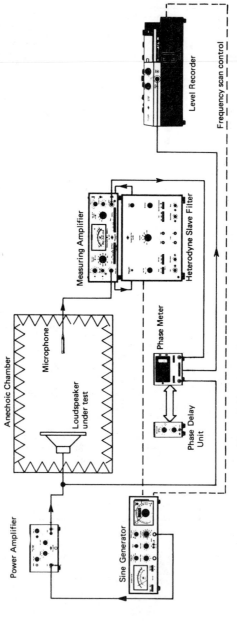

Figure 8.27 Set-up for loudspeaker phase measurements

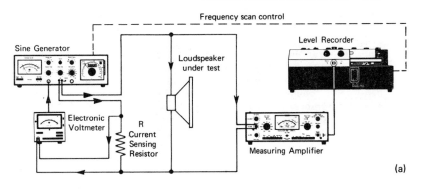

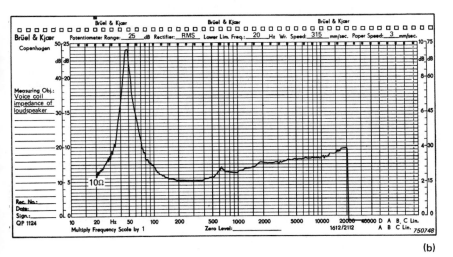

Figure 8.28 (a) Use of beat frequency oscillator as constant current generator. (b) Typical loudspeaker impedance curve. (Courtesy Bruel & Kjaer)

diaphragms and enclosure, via detailed analysis of the pulse response and its after effects. Some idea of these delayed resonances may be obtained without measurement, but the use of a fast Fourier transform programme in computer analysis has proved most revealing, and has considerably refined the evaluation of speaker transient performance. The computer system offers a refined averaging system which gives an excellent signal-to-noise ratio. An anechoic chamber is not necessary if the receiving microphone output is suitably gated before analysis, this eliminating local wall reflections as described in the section on gating.

Toneburst response

A less revealing method of examining the pulse, or more strictly the transient response of a speaker, employs gated sections of a steady state sine frequency, whereby judicious selection of gating period and tone frequency, delayed resonances may be investigated. A key point concerning the toneburst is the requirement for the envelope to consist of a whole number of cycles starting and stopping at the zero crossing point, so as to produce minimum asymmetric pulse disturbance. In addition, the measuring environment must be highly anechoic, or spurious reflections will interfere with the analysis. The recent introduction of gated pulse techniques has made simple toneburst testing largely redundant.

Sensitivity, efficiency and sound power output

Strictly speaking, sensitivity is an alternative way of quantifying loudness for a given input level. One standard, for example, is the acoustic output in dB ('A' weighted or unweighted: at 1 m on axis for 1 W electrical input. However, most sensitivity ratings are based on a nominal 1 W/8 Ω input of 2.83 V, regardless of the actual value of the usually complex loudspeaker impedance, and are in reality 'voltage sensitivity' ratings.

For true efficiency the total acoustic output should be measured by employing an integrating microphone arrangement — either a multiplex array or a rotating boom-mounted microphone, the latter used in conjunction with a reverberant chamber.

It nevertheless remains difficult to assess the real power input to a complex loudspeaker. A workable method involves the integration of the voltage and current of a random noise signal applied to the loudspeaker, the multiplication accomplished by a suitable wide-range measuring instrument, while the s.p.l. is simultaneously measured.

Electrical impedance

The Din standard for impedance is a sensible one and states that the modulus Z should not deviate more than ±20% from its nominal value of 4, 8 or 16 Ω, over the working frequency range (usually 8Ω).

The measurement is straightforward, involving the use of a current generator (usually a normal voltage sweep type which is fed to the loudspeaker via a high resistance, for example, 2 kΩ. The variation in voltage with frequency at the loudspeaker terminals reflects the variation of impedance. It is usual to substitute a known value resistor in place of the loudspeaker to confirm the scaling and, strictly speaking, a linear recording scale should be used.

Most recorders are fitted with logarithmic potentiometers, but a linear amplitude conversion chart will provide the remaining scale corrections required.

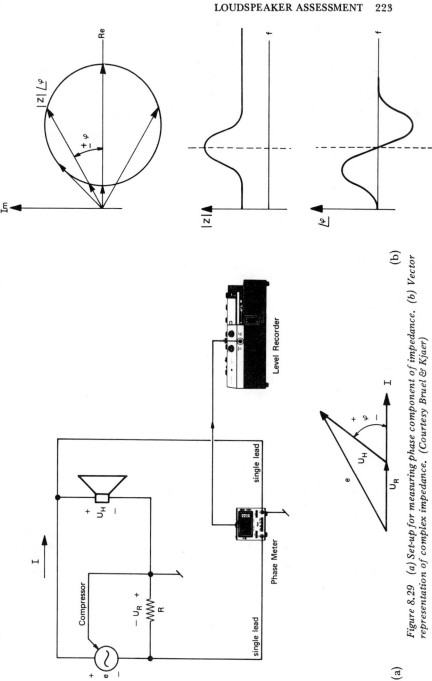

Figure 8.29 (a) Set-up for measuring phase component of impedance. (b) Vector representation of complex impedance. (Courtesy Bruel & Kjaer)

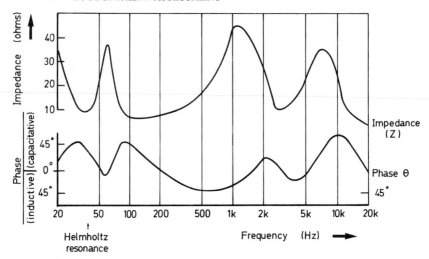

Figure 8.30   Impedance, magnitude and phase for a three-way reflex loaded system (crossovers at 3 kHz and 13 kHz, 18 dB/octave equalised)

The addition of a phase meter allows the recording of the phase component of impedance — an important factor where amplifier matching is concerned (Fig.8.29). Loudspeakers with large reactive impedances will often cause premature limiting and a consequent deterioration in sound quality when used with certain otherwise excellent power amplifiers. A 'compressor' generator also may be arranged to generate a constant current for accurate impedance measurement (Figs.8.28, 8.29 and 8.30).

Driver parameters

While the manufacturers who design their own drive units will hopefully retain complete information on their research, the system designer who works with drivers from several independent sources will need certain information which may not be readily available. A valuable source is the impedance curve, taken both in free air and with the driver mounted in a suitable air-tight box. The 2π frequency/amplitude characteristic may also be obtained as the unequalised voltage output from a low mass accelerometer temporarily fixed to the cone.

Suspension compliance — C_{MS} (metres/Newton)

This may be found by placing a known weight M on the diaphragm (horizontally disposed) and noting the resulting displacement d; for example, by using a travelling microscope. Now

$$C_{MS} = \frac{1}{s} = \frac{d}{Mg}$$

where g = gravitational acceleration and s = stiffness.

An alternative method of obtaining the compliance consists of noting the free air resonance f_0, and the in-box resonance f_c given with the driver mounted in a sealed unlined box of known volume, V_B. The air volume of the box has a compliance C_{AB}. The driver acoustic compliance C_{AS} is related to C_{MS} by S_D^2, the effective piston area, i.e.

$$C_{MS} = \frac{C_{AS}}{S_D^2}$$

$$\frac{C_{AS}}{C_{AB}} = 1.15 \left(\frac{f_c}{f_0}\right)^2 - 1$$

and

$$C_{AB} = \frac{V}{1.4 \times 10^5}$$

so

$$C_{MS} = \left(\frac{V_B}{S_D^2}\right) \left(\frac{10^{-5}}{1.4}\right) \left[\frac{1.15 f_c^2}{f_0^2} - 1\right]$$

The two compliance values may be compared to check for measurement accuracy.

Moving mass, M_D (kg)

This may be calculated from the free air or fundamental resonant frequency, f_0, which in turn may be taken from the peak in motional impedance. Having estimated the working diaphragm area (i.e. the projected moving area) by measurement, the equivalent radius, a, may be set. Then

$$M_D = \frac{1}{C_{MS}(2\pi f_0)^2} - 315 a^3$$

D.C. resistance (motor coil), R_c (ohms)

This may be measured by using a d.c. ohmmeter.

Coil inductance, L_c (henrys)

An a.c. impedance bridge may be used with the driver diaphragm clamped to prevent coil motion. The coil diaphragm inductance can also be calculated from the impedance curve without clamping if the unit is a low (<2%) efficiency type.

Mechanical resistance, R_{MS} *(of suspension components)*

The free air resonance peak is controlled by R_{MS}. Hence from the half-power or −3 dB voltage point on the impedance curve of f_0, and neglecting the small air load resistive component,

$$R_{MS} = \frac{2\pi f_0}{Q_M} (M_D + M_A)$$

where M_A = air load mass and

$$Q_M = \frac{f_0}{(f_1 - f_2)} \ (- 3 \text{ dB points}).$$

The impedance curve alone can thus provide much significant data on driver parameters and is often used in quality control sections of speaker production.

Electrical 'Q' factor, Q_E *(assuming zero generator impedance)*

Q_E is given by

$$Q_E = \frac{2\pi f_0 M_D R_C}{(Bl)^2}$$

Total 'Q' factor, Q_T

This is given by

$$\frac{1}{Q_T} = \frac{1}{Q_M} + \frac{1}{Q_E}$$

Flux density, B

This may be measured by using a flux probe in the magnet gap, although it requires the unit to be disassembled. Alternatively measurement of Bl and prior knowledge of l provides B.

Cone area, S_D *(square metres)*

This is derived via measurement and will include a percentage, usually 50% of the surround area (i.e. the projected area, not the actual cone surface area).

Force factor, Bl *(Newtons/ampere)*

This may be found by applying a known current I and measuring the excursion, d, ensuring that the moving axis is horizontal to exclude gravitational effects. Alternatively the driver may be placed horizontally, its rest position noted, and a known mass M applied. A d.c. current is then fed to the coil and adjusted until the extra mass is just balanced and the rest position attained. Then

$$Bl = \frac{9.8M}{I} \qquad \text{Wb/m (N/A)}$$

where M is in kg and I is in amperes.

Figure 8.31 is a reproduction of an informative specification published by a manufacturer of drive units.

8.4 SUBJECTIVE EVALUATION

The comparison of real sounds with those recorded and reproduced by a loudspeaker is obviously rewarding, but can be very difficult to achieve. There are two major problems, namely that of obtaining a consistent and repeatable live sound, and secondly, assembling a reliable and objective listening panel. It is virtually impossible for a single person, in particular the designer of the system under test, to make an unbiased assessment of its sound quality.

However, worthwhile methods for subjective sound evaluation are beginning to emerge. A number of factors need to be taken into consideration, some of the most important of which are outlined below (largely drawn from the IEC draft proposals referring to domestic loudspeakers).

Environment

A fairly well specified domestic listening room is suggested for test purposes, most studio control rooms in fact sufficiently approximate to average domestic conditions for this purpose. (The IEC proposals concern domestic reproducers, and other classes of system such as stage monitors will require an alternative arrangement.)

The room volume should be between 50 and 110 m^3, nominally 80 m^3, with a height of 2.75 ± 0.25 M, the preferred ratio of dimensions being L:B:H = 2.4:1.6:1. This gives the most even distribution of resonances, minimising room colouration effects. Within the range of heights suggested the ratio gives the following results for breadth, length, and volume.

KEF ISSUE 1075

Model B200
Specification Number SP1039

Low/mid range unit with visco-elastic damped
Bextrene diaphragm and high temperature coil
assembly, suitable for use where low distortion and
high power handling are required.

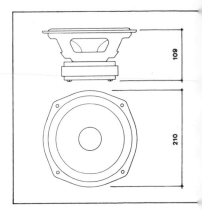

Net weight: 3.0 kg (6.6 lb)

Nominal impedance: 8Ω

Nominal frequency range: 25-3,500 Hz

Typical enclosure volumes:
Totally enclosed box 20-25 litres ($\frac{3}{4}$-1 cu ft)
Reflex 30-40 litres (1-1$\frac{1}{2}$ cu ft)

Power handling:
Continuous sine wave 25 V RMS (see note 1)
Programme 80 W (see note 2)

Magnet:
Flux density 1.2 T (12,000 gauss)
Total flux 1.17 x 10^{-3} Wb (117,000 Maxwells)

Sensitivity: Pink noise input for 96 dB SPL at
1 metre on axis 9 V RMS

Voice coil:
Diameter 32.6 mm (1$\frac{1}{4}$ in)
Inductance 0.25 mH
Max continuous service temperature (30 min) 250°C
Max intermittent temperature (5 sec) 340°C
Thermal time constant 4.5 seconds
Thermal resistivity (temp rise per applied Watt) 3°C/W
Nominal DC Resistance, R_{DC} 7.0Ω (tolerance ±5%)
Typical production spread 6.9±0.1Ω (see note 3)
Minimum impedance (in nominal frequency range)
7.1Ω at 190 Hz

Diaphragm:
Effective area, S_D 232 cm² (36 sq in)
Effective moving mass, M_D 20.2 gm (0.71 oz)
Max linear excursion, X_D 5 mm peak-peak (0.2 in)
Max damage limited excursion 20 mm peak-peak (0.8 in)

Free air resonance frequency, f_s:
Nominal 25 Hz (tolerance ±5 Hz)
Typical production spread 24±2.2 Hz (see note 3)

Total mechanical resistance of suspension, R_{MS}:
0.7 mech Ω

Suspension compliance, C_{MS}: 2.2 x 10^{-3} m/N
(2.2 x 10^{-6} cm/dyne)

Equivalent volume of compliance, V_{AS}: 130 litres
(7,930 cu in)

Force factor, Bl: 7.2 N/A

Damping:
Mechanical Q_M 4.4
Electrical Q_E 0.5
Total Q_T 0.45 (see note 4)

Notes
1 Continuous Power Rating (Pc).
$$Pc = \frac{V^2}{R}$$
V is the RMS voltage which can be applied to the
unit continuously without thermal overload of
the voice coil. At low frequencies the continuous
power rating of the speaker may be reduced
because of limitations imposed on diaphragm
excursion by the acoustic loading.
2 The programme rating of a unit is equal to the
maximum programme rating of any system with
which the unit may be safely used in conjunction
with the recommended dividing network and
enclosure.
The programme rating of any system is the
undistorted power output of an amplifier with
which the system may be satisfactorily operated
on normal programme over an extended period
of time.
3 "Typical production spread" is derived from
statistical analysis of a large number of units, and
is calculated to include 95% of all units.
4 $Q_M = \dfrac{2\pi f_s M_D}{R_{MS}}$ $Q_E = \dfrac{2\pi f_s M_D}{(Bl)^2/R_{DC}}$ $\dfrac{1}{Q_T} = \dfrac{1}{Q_M} + \dfrac{1}{Q_E}$

*Figure 8.31   An example of a useful data sheet for a drive unit. (Courtesy KEF
Electronics Ltd)*

TABLE 8.1(a). RECOMMENDED ROOM PROPORTIONS (I.E.C.)

Height (m)	Length (m)	Breadth (m)	Area (m²)	Volume (m²)	Room size
2.5	6.0	4.0	24.0	60.0	(min)
2.75	6.6	4.4	29.0	80.0	(mean)
3.00	7.2	4.8	34.0	101.0	(max)

TABLE 8.1(b) IDEAL ROOM RATIOS FOR DIFFERENT SIZED ROOMS (FROM OLSEN)

Room size	Length:	Breadth:	Height
Small	1.6:	1.25:	1
Medium	2.5:	1.6 :	1
Large	3.2:	1.25:	1

TABLE 8.2 RECOMMENDED REVERBERATION TIMES (I.E.C.)

Frequency (Hz)	Room reverberation time (seconds)
100	0.4 ↔ 1.0
400	0.4 ↔ 0.6
1000	0.4 ↔ 0.6
8000	0.2 ↔ 0.6

The test also requires reflecting walls* behind the loudspeakers with the opposing wall behind the listener absorptive. The ceiling should be untreated and the floor immediately adjacent to the speakers uncarpeted. Together with this formula, the reverberation time over the range 100 to 800 kHz should fit within the limits specified in Table 8.2.

Climatic conditions are also relevant with the optimal situation given as $20°C$, $±2°C$, relative humidity 65%, ±5%, and atmospheric pressure 860 to 1060 millibars.

Positioning

The systems should be positioned in accordance with the designer's or manufacturer's recommendations but if no such information is available, then a space of 1 m from the side walls and 0.5 m from the rear wall represents the minimum requirement. The main loudspeaker axis

* This can worsen stereo image quality for wide dispersion free standing models, and an absorbtive wall behind the enclosures is to be preferred.

should be elevated 1.25 m above floor level and facing the main listening areas. If a stereo pair is tested the left and right systems should be separated by at least 2.5 m, and if several pairs are simultaneously under test, no two speakers should be closer than 0.5 m.

Panel

The panel makeup depends upon the desired size, scope and application of the results, but for hi fi equipment, a sensible choice would include both male and female enthusiasts familiar with live performances as well as recording engineers and interested musicians. A maximum number of five panellists is suggested and the tester should be aware of the general hearing ability of each panel member, who should ideally be drawn from the twenty to forty-year age bracket. The combined results achieved will provide some averaging of the forward radiating characteristics of the system under test, while factors such as the exact placement of the panellists and the rotation of listening places should also be noted.

Programme material

The interaction between most types of music, its recording method and individual loudspeakers, is usually quite marked, and it is suggested that the test programme itself be regarded as a variable. Fairly short fifteen to thirty second programme sections, recorded with adequate pauses to allow the panel members to note their comments, have proved effective. This is satisfactory for A/B pairing. Single presentation methods require more extended programme, typically 2–5 minutes each.

Loudness

While the preferred listening level is that set by the average panellist, great care must be taken to ensure that the loudness of two speakers successively compared is carefully matched. If the response dissimilarities are severe this may be difficult to achieve and loudness adjustments for each programme section may then be necessary. Due regard for the overload point of both speaker and test amplifier is essential, and successive amplifier gain settings and the sound pressure are worth recording, the latter facilitated by a taped calibration signal and an 'A' weighted sound pressure reading

Duration

A single test session should not last longer than one hour, but with

TABLE 8.3. SCALE OF MARKING FOR SUBJECTIVE ACCURACY

Scale	Characterisation
10	Perfect reproduction, completely lifelike
9	Excellent fidelity
8	
7	Good
6	
5	Fair or average quality
4	
3	Poor
2	
1	Very poor reproduction
0	No resemblance to or connection with live sounds

TABLE 8.4. CLASSIFICATION OF SUBJECTIVE FREQUENCY BALANCE

Range	Frequency balance		
	Region	Deficiency or excess	Degree
Bass	low	+ or −	slight
	mid		moderate
	upper		severe
Mid	low	+ or −	slight
	mid		moderate
	upper		severe
Treble	low	+ or −	slight
	mid		moderate
	extreme		severe

Stereo image may also be rated provided that an accurate programme section (not multi-miked) is available, and the panel is instructed on how to assess image quality.

frequent short breaks and refreshments, good results may in practice be obtained over much longer periods.

Test procedure

Two procedures are discussed in the IEC draft proposals, namely a 'single stimulus'* or isolated judgement method where speakers are indi-

* Where the quality difference between loudspeakers is large, single presentation gives more consistent data by exploiting the long term experience and judgement of the panellists.[35]

TABLE 8.5. COLOURATION

Characterisation	Approximate frequency range
Boomy	50–80 Hz
Chesty, plummy	100–150 Hz
Boxy, hollow	150–300 Hz
Tubelike, tunnelly	400–600 Hz
Cuplike, honky	700–1.2 kHz
Nasal, hard	1.8–2.5 kHz
Prescence, upper hardness, wiry	2.5–5. 0 kHz
Sharp, metallic, sibilant	5.0–8.0 kHz
Fizzy, gritty	10–15 kHz

vidually scored, and the A/B method (where speaker A is compared with speaker B), which although more lengthy is less frustrating for the panel, since it affords a greater sensitivity to fine differences. In order to assess the degree of marking variation, the use of a 'control' or reference is valuable, not only on one occasion but repeated several times during the session to establish test continuity, and to gauge the consistency of marking.

A/B paired comparisons

Random presentation of the speakers is essential, particularly if a reference is involved, and the order of the programme sections should be similarly shuffled. The A and B systems must be given approximately equal periods of audition, and it is also important that the reversed B/A case is also presented. The human ear quickly becomes accustomed to the A or first sound, to the extent of filling in quite major irregularities. When the B sound is heard the ear superimposes the A compensation resulting in an initially incorrect judgement of B's abilities. Given sufficient time for the true assessment of B to become apparent, transfer back to A will give the opposite result. Usually the second or third reversal will result in a reasonably valid judgement of the relative merits of the two systems. Where 'A' is a live sound, these reversals, although not quite so important, are still worth including.

Ideally the comparison should be undertaken in stereo format but in practice the errors involved in stereo recording necessitate the adoption of monural recording. This also applies to the presentation which is best conducted using a single sample of each loudspeaker adjacent to the live sound.

The choice of sound presents some difficulties, an obvious one being the suggestion to use an orchestra. Single sounds can be effectively employed and these are easy to reproduce consistently and allow the panellists to make quick decisions. The radiation pattern of the source is an important consideration since typical loudspeakers are designed to radiate primarily in the forward plane particularly at higher frequencies, whereas most instruments are more or less omnidirectional. This problem can be overcome to a large degree by providing panel absorbers on the listening room wall behind the loudspeaker and the comparison live sound source.

Useful sounds include those of a percussive or transient nature such as a wood block xylophone, side drum, etc. A large 250 mm plain cymbal is often most revealing of high frequency problems. Acoustic guitar represents a 'mid' centred sound which accurate speakers can mimic very effectively. Though subject to more variation with time and mood, the human voice, particularly male, is a most revealing source spanning 100 Hz to 15 kHz. Distortions result in reduced intelligibility, exaggerated sibilants and the like.

The recording technique is important since the accuracy of the tape is vital to the comparisons. The location is preferably a large anechoic chamber with a low colouration flat response microphone employed at a generous distance from the source, typically 1–2 m.

An effective procedure consists of recording the live sounds in the form of short musical or verbal phrases lasting 3–5 seconds interspersed with pauses of slightly longer duration. On test the tape is run continuously to provide a constant background noise level, and the performer 'fills in' the pauses 'live' as they occur, repeating the preceeding reproduced phrase. Thus a number of A/B/A/B——— comparisons are possible with each sound. A total of 3–6 comparisons is usually sufficient and each sound presentation need only take a minute or two.

Scaling

An 11-point scale has given good results, where 0 and 10 represent the respective end points of extreme inaccuracy and excellence, with the numbers in between covering the marking range. The important characterisations can be variously termed as 'accuracy', 'neutrality', 'true to life' or 'true to nature'.

Other relevant characterisation of the perceived quality of high performance systems may also be employed, these including such terms as 'clarity', 'transparency' (the rendition of detail), 'frequency balance' (describing deficiencies or excesses of level in various parts of the frequency range) and 'colouration', with relevant comments drawn from an approved range of adjectives. As before these may be scaled from 0 to 10, and additional written comments can also be of value (Tables 8.3–8.5).

The results and their analysis

The reliability of the conclusions is proportional to the number of results. The IEC document suggests that two or more repetitions of each test combination is essential.

Various approaches may be adopted to the statistical analysis of the data: arithmetic mean, standard deviation and variance, to name but a few. Factors such as the test reliability, dependency on particular system/programme/panellist combinations and fatigue should all be taken into consideration. For example, in the unlikely event of no speaker or programme/speaker dependency, the analysis may be simplified, with averaging becoming the basic technique employed.

Psychological factors

Before leaving the subject of subjective testing, it is neeessary to make a few brief comments concerning its psychological and otological appects.

The listener or subject is sensitive to many qualities in sound reproduction to a greater or lesser degree, such as non-linear and other distortions, uniformity of frequency response, transient response, colouration and delayed resonances, phase, loudness, reverberation, stereo image and the related depth and position perception.

The most favourable or strongest subject reaction is understandably produced by a wide uniform frequency response, a suitable loudness appropriate to the listening environment and the programme, realistic imaging, minimal transient or delayed resonance colourations and a correct reverberation time.

While this may be classed as a basic response, it can be complicated by emotion. A particular foundness for an instrument on the part of the listener, or a certain section of programme, may induce a response out of proportion to that expected on an objective basis, and an error may result in either direction, depending upon the perception of either a pleasing or a disappointing effect. Likewise a subject's response will also depend on such factors as a recent or continuing illness; a cold, for example; his or her mood that day and whether a test occurs at the beginning or end of a session. Listening fatigue is a particularly important factor in this context. When differences are small it may be necessary to account for subject interaction. In a test on amplifier sound quality, such interaction in a listening panel was found to dominate the results[36]. However despite these many problems, subjective testing if planned carefully can be reliably executed and is essential to the advancement of loudspeaker quality. In the author's experience, it is only those models which have undergone successful and exhaustive critical audition prior to release that truly merit the classification 'high performance'.

REFERENCES

1. Allinson, R. F. and Berkovitz, R., 'The sound field in home listening rooms', *J. Audio Engng Soc.*, **20**, No.6 (1972)

2.   Moller, H., *Relevant Loudspeaker Tests,* Bruel and Kjaer Application Notes, 15–067

3.   Rosenberg, U., *Loudspeaker Measurement And Consumer Information,* Statens Provningsanstalt/Rapport (1973)

4.   Philips Electrical Ltd., *Measuring In The Living Room,* No.5697E

5.   Hughes, F. M. (a pseudonym for M. Colloms), 'A group test of thirty pairs of commercial loudspeakers', *Hi Fi For Pleasure,* 4, July, September and October (1976)

6.   Harwood, H. D., 'New BBC monitoring loudspeaker', *Wireless World,* March, April and May (1968)

7.   Shorter, D. E. L., 'A survey of performance criteria and design considerations for high-quality monitoring loudspeakers', *Proc. Instn. elect. Engrs.,* 105, p.B, November (1958)

8.   Fryer, P. A., 'Intermodulation distortion listening tests', *Proc. A.E.S. 50th Convention,* London, March (1975)

9.   Fryer, P. A., 'Distortions, can we hear them?' *Hi Fi News,* 22, No.7 (1977)

10. Harwood, H. D., 'Some aspects of loudspeaker quality', *Wireless World,* May (1976)

11. Heyser, R. C., 'Geometrical considerations of subjective audio', *J. Audio Engng Soc.,* 22, No.9 (1974)

12. Schroeder, M. R., 'Models of hearing', *Proc. Instn. elect. Engrs.,* 63, No.9, p.1332 et seq. September (1975)

13. MacKenzie, A., *Hi Fi Choice, Loudspeakers,* consumer report, Aquarius Books, London (1976)

14. Moir, J., 'Doppler distortion in loudspeakers', *Hi Fi News,* p.817 et seq.

15. Moir, J., 'Doppler distortion in loudspeakers', *Wireless World,* p.65 et seq. April (1974)

16. Stott and Axon, 'The subjective discrimination of pitch and amplitude changes', *Proc. Instn. elect. Engrs.,* 102, Pt.B, No.4 (1949)

17. Klipsch, P., 'Modulation distortion in loudspeakers', *J. Audio Engng Soc.* 18, No.1 (1970)

18. Bang and Olufsen, Phase Linearity

19. Bauer, B., 'Audibility of phase distortion', *Wireless World,* 27–28 March (1974)

20. Hansen, V. and Madson, E. R., 'On aural phase detection', *J. Audio Engng Soc.,* 22, No.1 (1974)

21. Harwood, H. D., 'Audibility of phase effects in loudspeakers', *Wireless World,* January (1976)

22. Heyser, R. C., 'Loudspeaker phase characteristics and time delay distortion', *J. Audio Engng Soc.,* 17, Nos.1 & 2 (1969)

23. Ishii, S. and Takahashi, K., 'Design of a linear phase multi-way system', *Proc. A.E.S. 52nd Convention,* October–November (1975)

24. Klipsch, P., 'Delay effects in loudspeakers', *J. Audio Engng Soc.,* 20, No.8 (1972)

25. Moller, H., *Loudspeaker Phase Measurements, Transient Response And Audible Quality,* Bruel and Kjaer Application Notes 15–090

26. Preis, D., 'Linear Distortion', *J. Audio Engng Soc.,* 24, No.5 (1976)

27. Staffedlt, S. H., 'Correlation between subjective and objective data for quality loudspeakers', *J. Audio Engng Soc.,* 22, No.6 (1974)

28. Cooke, R. E., 'Misleading measurements', *Hi Fi News,* October (1976)

29. Moller, H. and Thomson, C., *Electroacoustic Free-field Measurements In Ordinary Rooms, Using Gating Techniques,* (Bruel and Kjaer Application Notes, 15–107)

30. KEF Electronics Ltd., *Loudspeaker Testing Using Digital Techniques*, March (1975)
31. Moller, H., *Electroacoustic Measurements*, Bruel and Kjaer Application Notes (16–035)
32. Keele, D. B., 'Low frequency loudspeaker assessment by nearfield sound pressure measurement', *J. Audio Engng Soc.*, 22, No.3 (1974)
33. Berman, J. M. and Fincham, L. R., 'The application of digital techniques to the measurement of loudspeakers', *J. Audio Engng Soc.*, 25, No.6 (1977)
34. Suzuki, T., Morii, T. and Matsumara, S., 'Three-dimensional display for demonstrating transient characteristics of loudspeakers', *J. Audio Engng Soc.*, 26, Nos.7 and 8 (1978)
35. Colloms, M., *Hi-Fi Choice Loudspeakers III*, Bunch Books, London (1979)
36. Colloms, M., 'The panel game', *Hi-fi News*, No.11 (1978)

BIBLIOGRAPHY

Ashley, R. and Swan, M. D., 'Experimental determination of low frequency loudspeaker Parameters', *J. Audio Engng Soc.*, 17, No.5 (1969) 525

Baekgaard, E., 'Loudspeakers, the missing link', *Proc. A.E.S. 50th Convention*, London, March (1975)

Beranek, L., *Acoustics*, McGraw-Hill, London (1954)

Chapelle, P. H., 'The frequency response of loudspeakers on axis or power response', *Proc. A.E.S. 44th Convention*, February (1973)

Corrington, M. S., 'Correlation of transient measurements on loudspeakers with listening tests, *Loudspeaker Anthology, J. Audio Engng Soc.*, 1–25 (1979)

Eisler, H., *Psychological Measurement Of Acoustic Quality Of Sound Reproducing Systems By Means Of Factor Analysis*, University of Stockholm, No.188 (1965)

Harwood, H. D., 'Loudspeaker distortion associated with low frequency signals', *J. Audio Engng Soc.*, 20, No.9 (1972)

Heyser, R. C., 'Determination of loudspeaker signal arrival times', Pt.1, *J. Audio Engng Soc.*, 19, No.9 (1971);Pt.2, *J. Audio Engng Soc.*, 19, No.10 (1971)

—, *IEC Draft Proposals for Listening Tests*, Ref. SC29B/WG9; IEC, Technical Committee No. 12, Sub-committee No. 12A, Radio Recording Equipment Draft — Information Guide For Subjective Listening Tests (1975)

Jacobs, J. E. and Lee, C. J., 'Evaluation of acoustic systems utilising correlation techniques', *J. Audio Engng Soc.*, 26, No.5 (1978)

Jordan, E. J., Loudspeakers, Focal Press, London (1963)

Klipsch, P. W., 'A note on loudspeaker impedance and its effect on amplifier distortion', *J. Audio Engng Soc.*, 26, Nos.7 and 8 (1978)

Mantel, J., 'Definitions and measurement of fidelity and fidelity index of electroacoustical components and chains', *Proc. A.E.S. 44th Convention*, February (1973)

Olsen, H. F., *Modern Sound Reproduction*, Van Nostrand, New York (1972)

Shorter, D. E. L., 'Loudspeaker transient response: Its measurements and graphical representation', BBC *Quarterly Review*, 1, No.3 (1946)

Small, R. H., 'Simplified loudspeaker measurement at low frequencies', *J. Audio Engng Soc.*, 20, No.1 (1972)

Villchur, E., 'A method of testing loudspeakers with random noise input', *J. Audio Engng Soc.*, 10, No.4 (1962)

West, W. and MacMillan, D., 'The design of a loudspeaker', *Proc. Instn elect. Engrs.* (c. 1937)

Appendix 1. Electroacoustic standards

Below is given a list of the most relevant standards applied to electro acoustics. Many standards in the border area of this subject have been omitted and thus the list cannot be considered as being complete. Furthermore it is known that several Standards Organisations have relevant subjects under consideration which may outdate the present survey in a relatively short period.

Organi-sation	Number	Date	Status*	Short description
IEC	200	1966	S	Loudspeakers, frequency response, polar plot, resonant frequency, power handling, test conditions, standard baffle
ANSI	S.1.5	1963	S	Loudspeaker, impedance, frequency response, polar plot, distortion, efficiency, power handling, recommended
BS	1927	1953	S	Loudspeaker, physical dimensions, impedance and resonant frequency
BS	2498	1945	S	Loudspeakers, frequency response, distortion, efficiency polar plot, impedance, transient response conditions
IEC	268–5	1972	S	Loudspeakers**
DIN	45 500 sheet 1–3	Feb 1971	S	Loudspeakers, frequency response, power handling, distortion, music power
DIN	45 573 sheet 1	July 1962	S	Loudspeakers, test conditions and methods for type test
DIN	45 573 sheet 2	Jan 1969	S	Loudspeakers, power handling and life test
DIN	45 575	May 1962	S	Loudspeakers, standard baffle for measurements

*   S Standard
** BS5428 Pt II, 1977 (the power spectral curve is under amendment)

Appendix 2. Diaphragm phase characteristic and coincidence effect

While some discussion has been made of the effective velocity of sound in diaphragm materials, and its relationship to the loss of rigidity and breakaway from piston operation, measurement of many practical diaphragms has revealed essentially a minimum phase characteristic.

The described variation in velocity is founded on the supposition that bending waves are the significant factor in the progressive loss of rigidity at higher frequencies. However, the measured minimum phase character continues virtually to the second resonance region of the standard driver response, and this result implies that bending waves offer a minimal contribution up to this point.

With highly rigid structures such as the 'sandwich' cones formed from an expanded polystyrene or similar lightweight material stressed by stiff foil skins, another phenomenon caused by the coincidence effect may be present.

Coincidence occurs when the radiated wavelength in air equals the bending wavelength in a diaphragm or panel. Since the velocity in air is constant at lower frequencies coincidence is impossible but at higher frequencies a series of coincidences will develop as the changing velocity in the structure aligns at submultiples of the air velocity. At this stage phase shift appears between different areas of the diaphragm which may enhance or cancel specific break-up modes and in consequence result in sharp polar or beaming anomalies.

For a panel, for example in a loudspeaker enclosure, the angle of incidence may be critical in aligning the crest to crest air wavefront dimension relative to the panel bending model. At coincidence the panel is easily driven and the acoustic wave reappears on the other side unchanged in angle — the panel appears transparent for these frequencies and specific angles of coincidence.

Appendix 3. Higher order crossover networks and the maintenance of a constant axial directivity through the crossover range

With advanced loudspeaker designs, where drivers of uniform frequency response are utilised, the greatest remaining barrier lies in the response control through the crossover regions. The physical spacing between drivers, their different delays and crossover network phase shift, means that unless specifically allowed for, the directional properties through the crossover range will show undesired shifts in axis.

While even order networks do not provide a power sum to unity at the crossover frequency, the 4th order Butterworth does allow in-phase connection of the drivers throughout the frequency range. The steep slope, 24 dB/octave rolloff means that the theoretical 6 dB loss at the crossover frequency passes almost unnoticed, and may not be visible on the axial pressure response at all. Provided that the 4th order response is realised in terms of the final acoustic response of the drivers, and that their radiating centres are displaced in depth to account for driver and crossover delays, the system will possess a near minimum phase characteristic and the output from the adjacent drivers will remain in phase through the crossover region. Additionally the steep slopes rapidly attennuate any out of band irregularities in the drivers and thus minimise their effect on the prime response (Fig.A3.1).

Depth displacement of the drivers makes economic sense with a passive system, but where active crossovers are permissible greater freedom of driver mounting is allowed via the inclusion of electronic

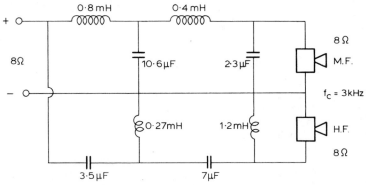

Figure A3.1 24 dB/octave passive crossover with constant axial response, drivers assumed constant 8 Ω (−6 dB at 3 kHz crossover point, scale to any frequency) (after Linkwitz)

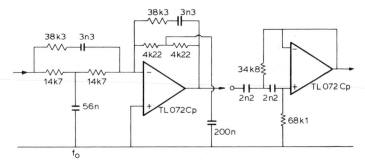

Figure A3.2

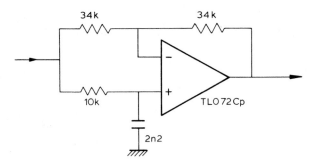

Figure A3.3

delay networks in the crossover. This may simplify the front baffle and remove the need for steps in the enclosure which might introduce diffraction anomalies.

Linkwitz[1] has looked closely at this aspect and discusses a number of useful techniques. In particular the inevitable problem of the fundamental resonance of a mid- or high-frequency driver may be incorporated in the system design as part of the 24 dB/octave high-pass filter sections. The rolloff below resonance is 12 dB/octave at the asymptote, and in addition to an electrical 12 dB/octave network, all that is required is a suitable equalisation stage to complete the 24 dB/octave high pass acoustic response function from the drivers.

Figure A3.2 shows a practical example of a high-pass section designed for a commonly used 25 mm fabric dome high frequency unit. The driver possesses a fundamental resonance, f_0 at 800 Hz, $Q = 0.9$, and the crossover point is placed at 1.5 kHz. The first network comprises a damped twin 'T' notch filter providing phase and amplitude control of f_0 together with a feedback generated peak compensation which applies gain and phase equalisation in conjunction with the input notch filter to generate an exact 12 dB/octave Butterworth response from the driver's acoustic output. The second network is simply the second cascaded 12 dB/octave network making 24 dB/octave total. The 110 mm diameter mid unit, mounted on a common flat panel has a radiation plane some 42 mm behind that of the HF driver. Three stages of delay for the latter are suggested, these each comprising an active unit of f_c = 7.2 kHz, in Fig.A3.3, τ = 22 μs $\equiv$ 14 mm.

Similar methods may be used to compensate for the relative time displacement between LF and MF drivers, and the first section of Fig. A3.2 is also applicable to the equalisation of the low frequency response. The system resonance may be compensated and the output extended to a lower frequency.

REFERENCE

1. Linkwitz, S. H., 'Loudspeaker System Design', *Wireless World*, **84**, No.1516 (1978)

INDEX